S/A-LEVEL Chemistry

Beavon

ESSENTIAL WORD **DICTIONARY**

Philip Allan Updates
Market Place
Deddington
Oxfordshire
OX15 0SE

Tel: 01869 338652
Fax: 01869 337590
e-mail: sales@philipallan.co.uk
www.philipallan.co.uk

ISBN 0 86003 375 9

Acknowledgements
I am grateful to Philip Cross for suggesting that I should write this dictionary, and to Patrick Fox for his editorial input. I have valued Doreen's considerable support during the writing of a work she is unlikely to read. Most particularly I wish to thank Peter Hughes at Westminster for his solid advice and clarifications, and my students over the years at Sherborne and at Westminster for theirs. Any infelicities that remain are, of course, their fault.

Printed by Raithby Lawrence & Co Ltd, Leicester

Introduction

This is a concise dictionary of key terms used in AS and A-level chemistry. Each word has been carefully chosen and is explained in detail to enhance your knowledge and understanding of this subject.

Many other dictionaries will contain words that are not relevant to students of AS and A-level chemistry. This dictionary, however, only lists the most important terms.

In the dictionary, each word is defined in up to four parts, as follows.

(1) A brief definition.
(2) Further explanation of the word.
(3) An example.
(4) An examiner's tip, such as where a word is commonly misunderstood, confused with another word, used in error, or found in conjunction with other words in the dictionary.

In many cases, all four parts are not needed and the entry has been amended accordingly. Finally, for each term it may be necessary to make a cross-reference to the words in italics in order to understand fully the entry you are reading.

Make extensive use of this 'essential words' dictionary. It could provide a significant boost to your chances of success in AS and A-level chemistry.

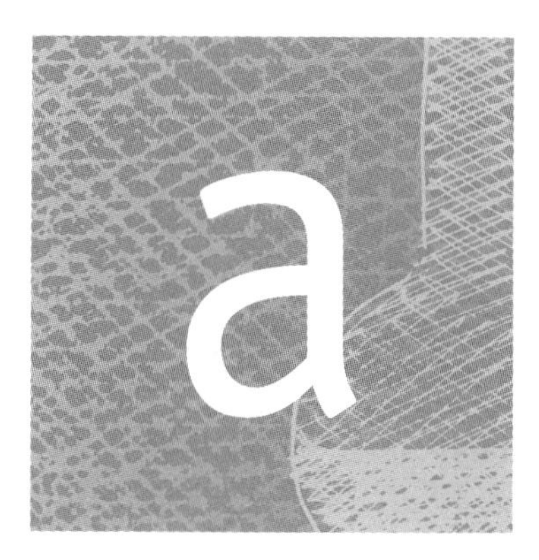

absolute temperature: the temperature measured on the Kelvin scale, where 0 K is the temperature at which the volume of an ideal gas is zero (an ideal gas would neither liquefy nor solidify).

- 0 K is –273.2°C. Absolute temperatures must always be used in thermodynamic and kinetic calculations. The size of the Kelvin degree is the same as the Celsius degree.
- ***TIP*** It is sufficiently accurate for most purposes to regard 0°C as 273 K. Note that there is no ° sign.

absorption: in spectroscopy, this is the loss of certain bands or wavelengths from the spectrum of light when transmitted through a coloured substance.

- The 'colour' need not be visible; absorption bands can occur in the *infrared*, visible or *ultraviolet* regions of the spectrum.
- ***e.g.*** White light passed through a solution of $[Cu(H_2O)_6]^{2+}$ ions comes out blue because of absorption bands in the red and green parts of the spectrum.
- ***TIP*** This is different from *adsorption*.

acceptor: an atom or ion that is electron deficient and which can therefore accept electron pairs from a donor molecule.

- Acceptor molecules are also called Lewis acids.
- ***e.g.*** Boron trifluoride, BF_3, has six electrons in the outer shell of the boron atom. It can accept a pair of electrons from ammonia molecules forming a *dative covalent bond*:

$$H_3N \longrightarrow BF_3 \text{ or } H_3N{:}BF_3$$

acid: according to the *Brønsted–Lowry acid–base theory*, an acid is a substance that donates *protons* when in solution.

- The solvent is usually water; in this solvent an acid, HA, will dissociate as follows:

$$HA(aq) + H_2O(aq) \rightleftharpoons H_3O^+(aq) + A^-(aq)$$

If dissociation is complete, the acid is a *strong acid*; otherwise it is a *weak acid*. The anion A^- is the conjugate base of the acid HA. (See also *conjugate acid–base pairs*.)

TIP There are other definitions of acid behaviour, but they are either very general or very specialised.

acid–base indicator: a *weak acid* whose molecule, HIn, is a different colour from its anion, In^-.

The position of the equilibrium

$$HIn(aq) \rightleftharpoons H^+(aq) + In^-(aq)$$

depends on the pH; large concentrations of H^+ (low pH) give the colour of HIn, low concentrations of H^+ (high pH) give the colour of In^-.

TIP Not all indicators change colour at the same pH; methyl orange changes around pH 3–4, whereas phenolphthalein changes around 9–10. It is important to know the form of the *titration curve* when selecting an indicator.

acid chloride (also called 'acyl chloride')**:** a compound of the form RCOCl, where R is an *alkyl* or *aryl* group.

Acid chlorides are reactive compounds and can be used to make *esters, poly(esters), amides* and *poly(amides).*

e.g. The commonest acid chloride is ethanoyl chloride, CH_3COCl, a fuming colourless liquid. Acid bromides are unimportant as they are more expensive and do not differ in any important properties.

TIP Ethanoyl chloride reacts violently with water, so do not write $CH_3COCl(aq)$!

acidic oxide: an oxide of a non-metal that reacts either with water to give acidic solutions, or, if insoluble, with alkalis to give salts.

e.g. Sulphur trioxide, SO_3, reacts (violently) with water to give sulphuric acid, H_2SO_4. In the blast furnace the acidic oxide SiO_2 reacts with calcium oxide, CaO, formed from the added limestone, to form slag, $CaSiO_3$. This is an acid–base reaction that does not take place in water.

acid salt: a salt produced from a polybasic acid (one that has more than one replaceable hydrogen ion per molecule) in which some of the hydrogen has not been replaced by other cations.

On dissolving in water, the hydrogen ions are dissociated to some extent and the solution is acidic.

e.g. Sodium hydrogen sulphate, $NaHSO_4$, from sulphuric acid; sodium dihydrogen phosphate, NaH_2PO_4 and disodium hydrogen phosphate, Na_2HPO_4, from phosphoric(V) acid, H_3PO_4.

activation energy: the minimum energy that a molecular collision must possess if the molecules are to react, that is to form a *transition state*.

TIP The activation energy is around 55 kJ mol^{-1} for those reactions whose rates roughly double for every 10°C rise in temperature. It can be calculated from the *Arrhenius equation* if the dependence of the reaction rate on temperature is known. Note that it is the collision energy that matters — it is not necessary for both molecules to possess the activation energy.

acyl chloride: see *acid chloride.*

addition reaction: in this reaction, molecules with double (or triple) bonds are saturated by the addition of a molecule across the double bond, which is therefore lost (see *saturated compound*).

■ Addition can occur with C=C, C=O, C=N, C≡N, and in inorganic systems with S=O — for example the action of water on SO_2. The reaction may be an *electrophilic addition* or a *nucleophilic addition.*

■ ***e.g.*** The addition of bromine to ethene is an electrophilic addition that is used as a test for C=C bonds:

$$H_2C{=}CH_2 + Br_2 \longrightarrow BrCH_2CH_2Br$$

In this test the yellow-orange colour of the bromine is lost and the mixture becomes colourless. The product, 1,2-dibromoethane, is used as an additive for leaded petrol. The latter material is still common across the world, even if not in the EU.

■ ***TIP*** The ability of *alkenes* to undergo addition makes them very valuable for making other chemicals. They are far too valuable to burn.

adsorption: the joining of one substance to the surface of another, usually temporarily.

■ ***e.g.*** Heterogeneous catalysis involves adsorption of the reactant molecules on to the surface of the catalyst, and chromatography involves some adsorption onto the stationary phase.

■ ***TIP*** This is distinct from *absorption,* where the substance added enters into the bulk of the material.

alcohol: an organic molecule containing the R–OH functional group, where R is an *alkyl* or *aryl* group. There are three varieties; primary (RCH_2OH), secondary (RR′CHOH) and tertiary (RR′R″COH).

aldehyde: a compound of general form RCHO, i.e. one that contains the functional group –CHO. R can be *alkyl* or *aryl.*

■ ***e.g.*** Ethanal, CH_3CHO, is the initial product of the oxidation of ethanol, whether chemically, using potassium dichromate and dilute sulphuric acid, or in the liver, using enzymes.

aliphatic compound: a compound that has carbon atoms in a chain rather than in an aromatic ring.

alkali metal: one of the metals of group 1: lithium, sodium, potassium, rubidium and caesium.

■ All alkali metals react with water to give strongly alkaline solutions of their hydroxides; the reactions become more violent as the size of the metal atom increases, the hydrogen evolved often igniting and setting the metal on fire:

$$2M(s) + 2H_2O(l) \longrightarrow 2MOH(aq) + H_2(g)$$

■ ***TIP*** The reaction of these metals with water or acids is not an acceptable method of making hydrogen.

alkaline earth metal: one of the metals of group 2: beryllium, magnesium, calcium, strontium and barium.

■ All alkaline earth metals react with water to give suspensions of their hydroxides (these are less soluble than group 1 hydroxides):

$$M(s) + 2H_2O(l) \longrightarrow M(OH)_2 + H_2(g)$$

The reaction of barium with water is hazardous.

■ ***TIP*** The reaction of these metals (apart from magnesium) with acids is not an acceptable way of making hydrogen.

alkane (also called 'paraffin')**:** a compound of general formula C_nH_{2n+2}.

■ The main constituents of petroleum, alkanes are important as fuels and as chemical feedstock for the manufacture of *alkenes* by *catalytic cracking*. They are not very reactive otherwise, though photochemical halogenation is important for solvent manufacture.

■ ***e.g.*** Methane, CH_4; ethane, C_2H_6; propane, C_3H_8.

■ ***TIP:*** The name 'paraffin' means 'of little affinity', i.e. unreactive.

alkene (also called 'olefin')**:** a compound of general formula C_nH_{2n} that does not contain a ring but does contain a C=C bond.

■ Formed from *alkanes* by *catalytic cracking*, they are much more reactive than alkanes and are not used as fuels, as their other uses are more important. Their characteristic reactions are *electrophilic addition* and polymerisation.

■ ***e.g.*** The simplest alkene is ethene, $CH_2{=}CH_2$.

■ ***TIP*** Always show the double bond explicitly in any structural formula. The general formula C_nH_{2n} also applies to the saturated cyclic hydrocarbons such as cyclohexane, C_6H_{12}. Hence the need to mention the C=C bond.

alkyl: a group derived from an alkane by the loss of a hydrogen atom.

■ ***e.g.*** Methane, CH_4, gives the methyl group, CH_3–.

allotropy: the ability of elements to exist in different physical forms or allotropes.

■ ***e.g.*** Red, white and black phosphorus; rhombic and monoclinic sulphur; diamond, graphite and the various *fullerenes*; oxygen, O_2 and ozone, O_3.

alloy: a substance whose properties are principally metallic but which consists of a mixture of metals or metals and one or more non-metals.

■ Most pure metals have some undesirable physical characteristics that can be improved on by alloying, which therefore makes the metals more useful.

■ ***e.g.*** Brass, an alloy of copper and zinc, is harder than copper alone but retains its good conductivity. Duralumin, an alloy of magnesium and aluminium, is not very dense but it is strong and is harder than aluminium alone. Steel is an alloy of iron with between 0.5% and 2% carbon, some of which is present in the alloy as a compound: cementite, Fe_3C.

aluminate ion: the reaction of aluminium hydroxide or aluminium oxide with sodium hydroxide solution gives a colourless solution containing aluminate ions.

■ The structure of aluminate ions is somewhat variable and may depend on the concentration of the solution and exactly how it is made. Any of the formulations $[Al(OH)_6]^{3-}$, $[Al(OH)_4]^-$ or AlO_2^{2-} is acceptable.

aluminium chloride: a substance whose structure depends on temperature.

- At room temperature it has a covalent *layer lattice*. Just below its sublimation temperature of 185°C it forms the dimer Al_2Cl_6; it sublimes as such, but increasing the temperature of the vapour causes dissociation into $AlCl_3$. Aluminium chloride reacts with water to give acidic solutions.
- ***TIP*** Do not suggest that aluminium chloride is $AlCl_3$ at low temperature and then dimerises — it is not so. The acidity is due to *deprotonation* of the hydrated aluminium ion:

$$[Al(H_2O)_6]^{3+}(aq) + H_2O(l) \longrightarrow [Al(H_2O)_5(OH)]^{2+}(aq) + H_3O^+(aq)$$

amalgam: an *alloy* of a metal with mercury.

- Amalgams may be solid or liquid.
- ***e.g.*** Dental amalgam contains mercury and tin with smaller amounts of other metals.

amide: a compound of general formula $RCONH_2$.

- Amides are derivatives of *carboxylic acids* and are made by the action of ammonia on an *acid chloride*. They are not basic because the lone pair of electrons on the nitrogen atom is made less available by the electron-withdrawing carbonyl group.
- ***e.g.*** The simplest amide is ethanamide, CH_3CONH_2. It is popularly believed to smell of mice.

amine: amines are of three types: primary, of form RCH_2NH_2; secondary, of form RNHR′; and tertiary, of form R(R′)NR″.

- All are basic and will react with aqueous solutions of acids to form amine salts.
- ***TIP*** The terms primary, secondary and tertiary do not signify the same thing here as they do for *alcohols*. In alcohols the structure of the carbon skeleton is different but the functional group, –OH, remains the same.

amino acid: the amino acids of most significance are the α-amino acids that are used to make proteins.

- They have the structure:

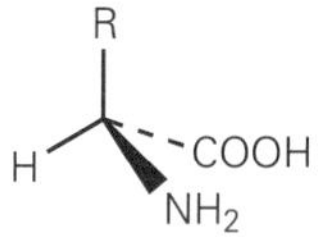

R
H
COOH
NH_2

and apart from the case of glycine, where R is a hydrogen atom, the amino acids are *chiral molecules*. In the solid and in solution the molecule is more accurately represented as a dipolar ion or *zwitterion*:

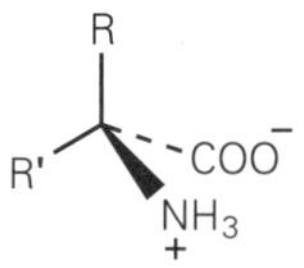

R
R'
COO^-
NH_3^+

In consequence, the substances have higher melting temperatures than might be expected from their size, as the interactions between molecules are electrostatic between full + and – charges.

ammine complex: a *complex ion* where the central transition metal ion has *ligands*, some or all of which are ammonia.

■ ***e.g.*** One of the best-known is the deep blue ammine complex formed when concentrated ammonia is added to a solution of copper(II) ions. Its structure is:

$$\left[Cu(NH_3)_4(OH_2)_2 \right]^{2+}$$

■ ***TIP*** Do not confuse ammine with *amine*, which is a compound of type RNH_2.

ammonia, NH_3: the simplest *hydride* of nitrogen.

■ It is basic and is the most water-soluble gas.

ammoniacal silver nitrate solution: addition of aqueous ammonia solution to silver nitrate solution gives first a greyish precipitate of silver oxide, which then reacts further to give a solution of diamminesilver(I), $[Ag(NH_3)_2]^+$.

■ This solution will oxidise *aldehydes* to *carboxylic acids* on warming, being reduced itself to give a silver mirror.

■ ***TIP*** *Tollen's reagent* is not the same material; it uses sodium hydroxide solution to precipitate the silver oxide initially. Tollen's reagent will work at room temperature. Solutions of diamminesilver(I) should not be kept; they deposit explosive silver azide on standing.

ammonium ion, NH_4^+: the ion formed on addition of acid to ammonia.

■ This ion is the conjugate acid of the base NH_3.(See also *conjugate acid–base pairs.*)

amount of substance: the number of moles of substance that you have.

■ ***TIP*** In chemistry, 'amount' should always be used in this technical sense rather than in its everyday sense. In calculations avoid writing 'number of moles of iron = 8.5×10^{-3} mol'; instead write 'amount of iron = 8.5×10^{-3} mol'.

amphoteric oxide: an oxide that will react with either an acid or a base to give a salt.

■ ***e.g.*** The oxides of aluminium, zinc, chromium(III), tin(II) and tin(IV), and lead(II) and lead(IV) are all amphoteric oxides.

anion: a negative ion, which migrates to the positive electrode or anode in *electrolysis*.

anode: the electrode at which *oxidation* occurs in electrochemical processes.

■ In an electrolytic cell the anode is the positive electrode, where processes such as

$$2Cl^- \longrightarrow Cl_2 + 2e^-$$

occur. In an electrochemical cell the anode is the source of electrons, because oxidation has occurred in that part of the cell. It is therefore the negative pole of the cell.

■ ***TIP*** At an **A**node, oxid**A**tion occurs.

anodising: a technique used to give aluminium objects a protective coat of oxide to make them more resistant to corrosion than un-anodised aluminium.

■ The technique involves making the aluminium object the *anode* in a electrolytic cell whose electrolyte is a solution of potassium chromate(VI) in dilute sulphuric acid. Dyes can be incorporated into the bath to give a coloured oxide layer.

aqua-ions of transition metals: transition metal ions in aqueous solution are bonded to a number, usually six, of molecules of water. Hexaqua ions are also found with some non-transition metals, for example $[Al(H_2O)_6]^{3+}$.

■ The bonds are dative covalent bonds from the water *ligands,* the structures of the ions being octahedral.

■ ***e.g.*** Hexaquairon(II) is typical:

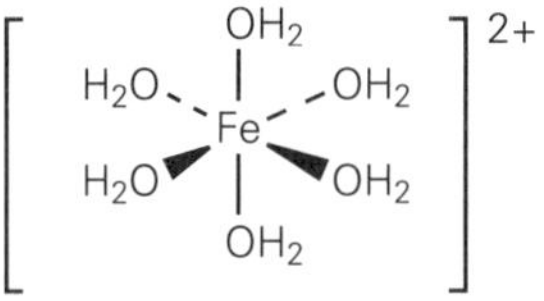

OH_2
H_2O OH_2
Fe
H_2O OH_2
OH_2
2+

aqueous solution: a *solution* in which water is the *solvent* — the *state symbol* for such solutions is (aq).

■ ***TIP:*** The state symbol for water itself is (l); (aq) is used only for the material that is dissolved in water.

aromatic compound: a compound that contains a benzene ring, or another ring that shows similar properties to that of benzene because of *delocalisation of electrons.*

Arrhenius equation: an equation that links the rate constants for a reaction obtained at different temperatures to the *activation energy* for the reaction.

■ For two different values of rate constant, k_1 and k_2, at temperatures T_1 and T_2 the Arrhenius equation is:

$$\ln(k_1/k_2) = (E_a/R)(1/T_2 - 1/T_1)$$

where E_a is the activation energy for the reaction, and R is the *gas constant.* Temperatures must be in K.

■ ***TIP*** Note that whichever k is in the numerator of the left-hand side (and it does not matter which one is), its corresponding temperature appears last in the brackets on the right-hand side. If more than two sets of data are available, a graphical method can be used; a plot of $\ln k$ (y-axis) vs $1/T$ (x-axis) gives a straight line of slope E_a/R. The value of E_a obtained will be in $J\ mol^{-1}$.

aryl: a group derived from an aromatic compound by loss of a hydrogen atom.

■ ***e.g.*** The simplest example is *phenyl,* C_6H_5-.

asymmetric carbon atom: a common term for a carbon atom that is attached to four different groups of atoms.

■ As long as the molecule that ensues is not superimposable on its mirror image (always true if the molecule contains only one asymmetric carbon atom), it will be a *chiral molecule*.

atom: the smallest part of an element that retains the chemistry of the element.

atomicity: the number of atoms in a molecule.

■ ***e.g.*** H_2 has an atomicity of 2.

atomic number: the number of protons in the nucleus of an atom.

■ ***TIP*** Although the proton number is the same as the number of electrons in a neutral atom, electrons do not figure in the definition of atomic number.

atomic radius: half the distance of closest approach of atoms in an element's structure.

■ This may differ if the element shows *allotropy,* e.g. carbon.

aufbau principle (also called 'building-up principle')**:** the principle by which the *electron configuration* of atoms can be derived by putting electrons into atomic *orbitals* in order of increasing energy.

■ ***TIP*** Aufbau means 'building up'.

average bond enthalpy (also called 'mean bond enthalpy')**:** the heat energy required to break one mole of a given type of bond.

■ It is 'average' because a typical value is quoted; however, the actual value for a particular bond will depend on the molecular environment and will therefore deviate somewhat from the average.

■ ***e.g.*** The average bond enthalpy for the C=O bond is around 740 kJ mol^{-1}; in methanal, HCHO, it is 695 kJ mol^{-1} and in carbon dioxide it is 805 kJ mol^{-1}.

Avogadro constant: the number of particles present in one mole of substance.

■ Its value is 6.02×10^{23} mol^{-1}, near enough 6×10^{23} mol^{-1} for most purposes. The particles depend on the substance, and may be ions, molecules or atoms.

azeotrope: a mixture of liquids that will distil without changing in composition.

■ The composition of an azeotrope depends on the atmospheric pressure. It is not possible to separate all of the components of an azeotrope by fractional distillation.

■ ***e.g.*** A well-known azeotrope is a mixture of ethanol and water. Ethanol cannot be completely separated from aqueous solution — the azeotrope consists of about 95% ethanol and 5% water.

azo dye: a *dye* that contains the azo linkage: –N=N–.

■ Azo dyes were developed accidentally by William Perkin in the 1880s. They are made by reacting a primary aromatic amine with nitrous acid, and then reacting the resulting *diazonium compound* with an alkaline solution of a *phenol*. They are brightly coloured and do not readily fade on exposure to light.

e.g. The reaction producing the bright red phenylazo-2-naphthol is typical:

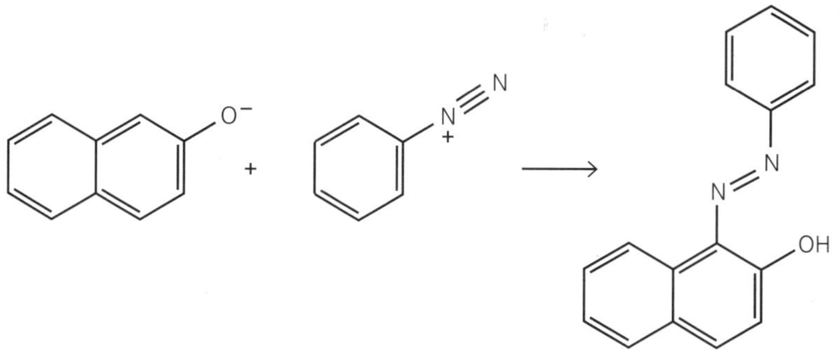

O⁻ + N≡N⁺ → N=N, OH

base: according to the *Brønsted–Lowry acid–base theory,* a base is a *proton* acceptor.

- Bases include hydroxide, carbonate and sulphide ions, as well as ammonia and water. The strength of a base is a measure of how readily it will accept H^+ ions. Acids produce bases when they dissociate.
- ***e.g.*** For the system $HA(aq) + H_2O(l) \rightleftharpoons H_3O^+(aq) + A^-(aq)$, the acid HA donates a proton to water, which is behaving as a base; this gives the hydroxonium ion, which can act as an acid, and the anion A^-, which can act as a base. If the acid HA is a *strong acid,* its conjugate base A^- is weak. (See also *conjugate acid–base pairs.*)

basic oxide: a metal oxide that reacts with an acid to give a salt.

- ***e.g.*** $CaO(s) + 2HCl(aq) \longrightarrow CaCl_2(aq) + H_2O(l)$

bauxite: the principal ore of aluminium.

- It is variable in composition, containing 50–70% aluminium oxide, 3–25% iron(III) oxide, 1–7% silicon dioxide, 2–3% titanium dioxide and 12–40% water.

Benedict's reagent: a solution of copper(II) ions complexed with citrate ions and made alkaline with sodium carbonate.

- On heating with aldehydes it gives a red or orange-red precipitate of copper(I) oxide.
- ***TIP*** Benedict's reagent is used instead of *Fehling's solution,* which does the same thing, because it does not have to be mixed immediately before use and is much less caustic than Fehling's solution, which contains NaOH.

benzene, C_6H_6: a ring compound often represented as having three double bonds between alternate carbon atoms.

- The electrons in these bonds are, however, delocalised around the ring and the reactions of benzene are not those of an alkene. Instead of *electrophilic addition,* benzene undergoes *electrophilic substitution,* which preserves the delocalised electron structure.
- ***TIP*** The structure of benzene was discovered by Friedrich August Kekulé von Stradonitz, and the common representation of benzene shown below (left) is

the one developed by him. As it is well known that this structure means benzene, it is not 'wrong' to use it. However, many people prefer the structure on the right, as it emphasises the fact that the electrons are delocalised. Remember that it is not always correct to extend this use when several rings are fused together.

benzenediazonium chloride: a compound formed by the action of nitrous acid, HNO_2, on phenylamine in concentrated hydrochloric acid, HCl, at 0–5°C.

▪ It has the structure

$$C_6H_5-\overset{+}{N}\equiv N \quad \overset{-}{Cl}$$

and is useful for making *azo dyes* as well as a number of other aromatic compounds.

▪ ***TIP*** Note that the positive charge is on the left-hand nitrogen atom.

bimolecular reaction: if two species collide in the *rate-determining step* of a reaction, that reaction is bimolecular.

▪ ***e.g.*** The S_N2 reaction of bromomethane and hydroxide ions is bimolecular:

$$H\overset{-}{O}{:} + CH_3{-}Br \longrightarrow [HO\cdots CH_3\cdots Br]^- \longrightarrow HO{-}CH_3 + {:}\overset{-}{Br}$$

▪ ***TIP*** The molecularity of a reaction and the *order of reaction* are not necessarily the same; if the rate-determining step in a reaction is not the first step, then the order and the molecularity will be different.

binary compound: a compound that contains only two elements.

binary liquid mixture: a mixture of two *miscible liquids*.

bleach: common household bleach is a solution of sodium chlorate(I) (sodium hypochlorite), NaOCl.

▪ It is made by electrolysis of concentrated sodium chloride solution and allowing the chlorine and sodium hydroxide produced to react at room temperature:

$$2NaOH + Cl_2 \longrightarrow NaOCl + NaCl + H_2O$$

▪ ***TIP*** The bleaching action of NaOCl, and of chlorine itself, is due to the oxidation of the coloured material.

boiling temperature (also called 'boiling point')**:** the temperature at which the *vapour pressure* of the liquid is the same as the external atmospheric pressure.

■ Boiling temperature is variable, so the values quoted in tables usually refer to a standard pressure of 1 atm or 101.325 kPa. It is also the temperature at which a liquid is in equilibrium with its vapour at the standard pressure.

bomb calorimeter: a device used to measure energy changes that occur when substances are burnt in excess oxygen under pressure in a sealed container.

■ The heat evolved is used to heat a known mass of water. From such experiments the *enthalpy of combustion* at constant volume, ΔU, can be found. This can be corrected to give the enthalpy of combustion at constant pressure, ΔH.

bond enthalpy: the *enthalpy change* when one mole of a bond is broken.

■ *Average* or *mean bond enthalpies* are usually used in calculations.

■ ***e.g.*** To break one mole of Cl–Cl bonds requires +242 kJ; this is the bond enthalpy of chlorine.

■ ***TIP*** Bond enthalpies, being average values, will give only a rough idea of the enthalpy change for a reaction.

Born–Haber cycle: a thermochemical cycle that relates the *enthalpy of formation* of an ionic substance to the *ionisation energy* (or energies) of the metal ion, the *electron affinity* (or affinities) of the non-metal, the *enthalpies of atomisation* of both the metal and the non-metal, and the *lattice energy* of the solid.

■ ***TIP*** The Born–Haber cycle gives the actual (experimental) value for the lattice energy, rather than one obtained from the assumption of wholly ionic bonding.

Brady's reagent: a solution of 2,4-dinitrophenylhydrazine in either hydrochloric or phosphoric acid.

■ It is used to test for the >C=O group in aldehydes or ketones. When it is mixed with compounds containing this group, an orange solid is precipitated. The derivatives are easy to purify and their melting temperatures are well-documented and can often be used to identify the carbonyl compound.

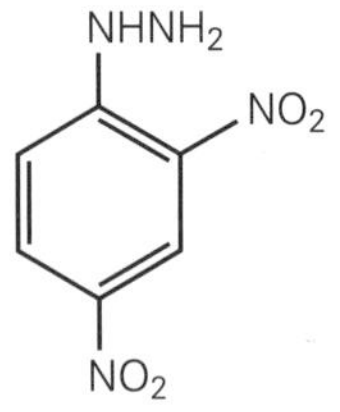

$NHNH_2$

NO_2

NO_2

■ ***TIP*** It is better to refer to the reagent by its chemical name — 2,4-DNP will often do. Carbonyl groups in acids, RCOOH, or amides, $RCONH_2$, do not react with 2,4-dinitrophenylhydrazine.

branched chain: carbon-containing compounds in which the carbon atoms are not arranged linearly but have branches.

■ ***TIP*** A branch is often shown by the use of brackets in a formula, so keeping it all on one line.

$CH_3CH_2CH(CH_3)CH_3$ is the same as

$$H_3C-CH_2-CH(CH_3)-CH_3$$

There is no need to use the bracket style in handwritten material — it was a device developed to make things easy for printers when text was set in movable type. Give the displayed structure.

brine: a concentrated solution of sodium chloride.

- Brine is used to make sodium hydroxide, NaOH, and sodium chlorate(I), NaOCl, a *bleach*.
- **TIP** *Seawater* is not brine, and is far too dilute for the manufacture of sodium hydroxide or sodium chlorate(I) by electrolysis. (See also *diaphragm cell.*)

bromine water: an aqueous solution of bromine that contains hydrated bromine molecules, HBr and HOBr:

$$Br_2(aq) + H_2O(aq) \rightleftharpoons HBr(aq) + HOBr(aq)$$

- It is commonly used to test for the presence of a carbon–carbon double bond, which turns the yellow/orange solution colourless.

Brønsted–Lowry acid–base theory: the theory that defines acids as proton donors and bases as proton acceptors.

- It is by far the commonest view of acid–base behaviour in aqueous solutions.
- ***e.g.*** hydrogen chloride on dissolving in water gives H_3O^+ ions:

$$HCl(g) + H_2O(l) \longrightarrow H_3O^+(aq) + Cl^-(aq).$$

The H_3O^+ ions will then donate their proton to a base, H_3O^+ therefore being an acid:

$$H_3O^+(aq) + OH^-(aq) \longrightarrow 2H_2O(l)$$

Buchner funnel: a funnel used to filter solutions quickly with the aid of a suction pump.

- Buchner funnels are usually made of porcelain and have a flat perforated base on which the filter paper is placed. The liquid is sucked through by a vacuum pump.

buckminsterfullerene, C_{60}: a spherical allotrope of carbon having 20 hexagonal and 12 pentagonal rings — exactly as in a football.

- All 60 carbon atoms in the molecule occupy the same environment. The determination of the structure of C_{60}, a reddish-orange material soluble in benzene, relied heavily on instrumental techniques such as *mass, IR, UV* and *NMR* (^{13}C) *spectroscopy.*
- **TIP** The story of the discovery of C_{60} is a colourful one, and illustrates well the disappointments that can go with research. The structure of C_{60} was published by Donald Huffmann (University of Arizona) and Wolfgang Kratschmer (University of Heidelberg) a few days before Harry Kroto (University of Sussex). The three men shared the Nobel prize for their work.

buffer: a substance that keeps the pH of a solution almost constant if small amounts of acid or base are added, or if the solution is diluted.

- Buffers usually consist of a weak acid and the sodium salt of that weak acid.
- ***e.g.*** A mixture of sodium citrate and citric acid is used to buffer the pH of jam at a value that discourages the growth of mould.
- ***TIP*** A buffer does not keep the pH completely constant, and it is important that only small amounts of acid or base contaminant are involved.

building-up principle: see *aufbau principle.*

calcite (also called 'calcspar', 'Iceland spar', 'dogtooth spar')**:** the form of calcium carbonate, $CaCO_3$, responsible for deposits of limestone, chalk and marble.

calorific value: the amount of heat evolved by a unit mass of a substance (or of a unit volume of gas) being burnt.

■ ***TIP*** The name comes from the obsolete unit of heat, the calorie; the value would be given in kJ g^{-1}, kJ kg^{-1} or kJ m^{-3}.

calorimeter: apparatus enabling the combustion of a material so that the heat evolved is absorbed in a surrounding water bath whose temperature rise can be measured.

carbanion: an ion bearing a negative charge on a carbon atom.

■ They are very reactive.

■ ***e.g.*** *Grignard reagents,* such as CH_3MgX, effectively act as $CH_3^-MgX^+$, where the carbanion is a strong nucleophile.

carbocation: an ion containing a positively charged carbon atom.

■ ***e.g.*** In the *S_N1* substitution reaction of 2-bromo-2-methylpropane the first step is the *heterolytic fission* of the C–Br bond to give the carbocation $(CH_3)_3C^+$ and bromide ion Br^-.

$$(H_3C)(CH_3)_2C{-}Br \xrightarrow{\text{slow}} H_3C{-}\overset{+}{C}(CH_3)_2 + :\overset{-}{Br}$$

■ ***TIP*** In reaction mechanisms, don't show curly arrows going to or coming from charges (see *S_N1*).

carbohydrate: a compound of carbon, hydrogen and oxygen having the approximate formula $C_x(H_2O)_y$.

■ Although carbohydrates do not contain water as such, they can be dehydrated by concentrated sulphuric acid to give carbon (see *dehydration*).

■ ***e.g.*** Sugars, starches and cellulose are carbohydrates. Many of these are *chiral molecules.*

carbonate ion, CO_3^{2-}: an ion formed in small amounts when carbon dioxide is dissolved in water.

- Carbonates react with acids to give a fizz of carbon dioxide, and are widely distributed in nature, mostly as $MgCO_3$ or $CaCO_3$.
- ***e.g.*** The ionic equation for the reaction of carbonates with acid is

$$CO_3^{2-} + 2H_3O^+ \longrightarrow CO_2 + 3H_2O$$

- ***TIP*** Only carbonates or hydrogen carbonates fizz when acid is added to them.

carbon dioxide, CO_2: the oxide formed when carbon or carbon-containing compounds burn in excess oxygen.

- It is popularly associated with global warming. It is also the gas from which all organic compounds are derived, as all come originally from photosynthesis. The molecule is linear O=C=O and is non-polar, because the dipoles in the bonds are opposed and cancel. It forms an acidic solution called carbonic acid but this contains very few H_2CO_3 molecules; the undissociated part is primarily hydrated carbon dioxide.

carbon monoxide, CO: the oxide of carbon formed (always with some CO_2) when carbon or carbon-containing substances burn in limited oxygen. It is poisonous, binding very strongly with haemoglobin in blood and preventing it from carrying oxygen. Carbon monoxide poisoning can be treated by administering high oxygen concentrations, which displaces the carbon monoxide.

carbon tetrachloride, CCl_4 (more properly called 'tetrachloromethane')**:** a substance that is used widely, but decreasingly, as a *solvent*; it is inert to water, unlike the tetrahalides of other group 4 elements.

carbonyl compound: an organic compound that contains the >C=O group; the two other carbon bonds are attached to hydrogen atoms or to *alkyl* or *aryl* groups.

- ***e.g.*** HCHO is methanal, CH_3CHO is ethanal, and both are *aldehydes*; CH_3COCH_3 is propanone and is the simplest of the *ketones*.
- ***TIP*** Numerous other compounds, such as carboxylic acids, acid chlorides and acid amides, contain the carbonyl group, but in each case the characteristic reactions of the group are masked. They do not, for example, react with 2,4-dinitrophenylhydrazine (*Brady's reagent*).

carboxylic acid (also called 'fatty acid')**:** a compound of the form RCOOH.

- They are weakly acidic if soluble in water, otherwise they react with bases to give salts. The name 'fatty acids' is sometimes used because they were originally obtained from the reaction of animal or vegetable fats with sodium hydroxide solution. The sodium salts of longer-chain fatty acids are soaps.
- ***e.g.*** HCOOH is methanoic or formic acid, found in nettles and red ants; CH_3COOH is ethanoic acid and is found in vinegar; $C_{17}H_{35}COOH$ is stearic acid, its sodium salt being widely used as a soap. Propionic acid, the original name

for propanoic acid, CH_3CH_2COOH, comes from the French 'propionique', meaning 'from fat'.

carcinogen: a substance that induces cancer.

- ***e.g.*** There is a huge variety of carcinogenic substances, including asbestos, 2-naphthylamine, and many aromatic compounds found in soot and in tars (including cigarette tar).
- ***TIP*** Benzene is somewhat carcinogenic, which is why it is not used in schools. This does not mean that all aromatic compounds are carcinogenic. Data have to be obtained for individual compounds, as small differences in structure make enormous differences to carcinogenicity:

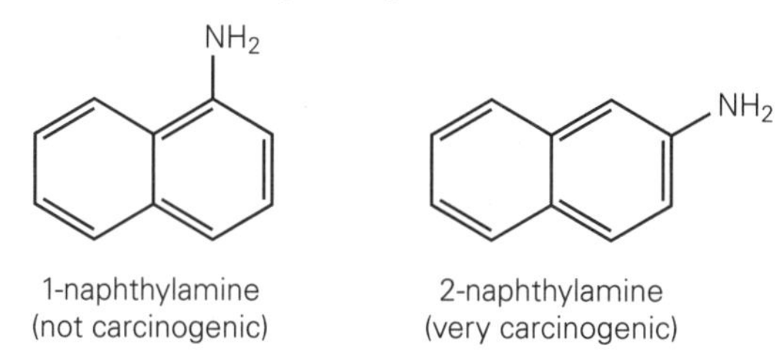

cast iron (also called 'pig iron')**:** the solidified iron direct from the blast furnace.

- Containing about 4% carbon, it is very brittle but very tough in certain applications, such as manhole covers.

catalyst: a substance that increases the rate of a reaction without itself being used up in the reaction.

- It functions by providing an alternative mechanism to that of the uncatalysed pathway, this mechanism having a lower *activation energy*.
- ***e.g.*** Many organic reactions are catalysed by acid, for example esterification. Vanadium(V) oxide catalyses the oxidation of SO_2 to SO_3 by oxygen in the *contact process*, and iron catalyses the reduction of nitrogen by hydrogen to give ammonia in the *Haber process*.
- ***TIP*** The catalyst changes the mechanism for the reaction to one of lower activation energy. It does not lower the activation energy for the original mechanism.

catalytic cracking: a process in which long-chain alkanes are passed over a heated catalyst, such as silica or alumina, to break them down into smaller molecules, some of which are unsaturated.

- Used to give useful products (fuels and alkene feedstocks) from long-chain compounds which themselves have limited usefulness.

cathode: the negative electrode at which reduction occurs in *electrolysis*.

- In an *electrochemical cell* the cathode, being the electrode that puts electrons into the electrolyte, is the positive pole of the cell.
- ***e.g.*** The cathode reaction in the electrolysis of aluminium oxide is

$$Al^{3+} + 3e^- \longrightarrow Al$$

TIP At the **C**athode, redu**C**tion occurs.

cation: a positively charged ion, discharged at the *cathode* (negative electrode) of an electrolytic cell.

e.g. Metals form cations, such as Na^+; this positive ion formation is the characteristic property of metals. Some cations are non-metallic, such as NH_4^+, and many are complex, such as $[Cu(H_2O)_6]^{2+}$.

cell: see *electrochemical cell.*

Celsius scale (formerly called 'Centigrade scale')**:** the temperature scale where the fixed points are the freezing temperature of water at 0°C and the boiling temperature of water at 100°C.

chain reaction: a sequence of reactions, each using the products of the previous reaction.

Commonly such reactions produce a radical, which is then used to produce another, and then another of the original radicals.

e.g. The reaction between chlorine and methane in ultraviolet light:

Initiation step, not part of the chain:

$$Cl_2 \longrightarrow 2Cl\bullet$$

Propagation steps, the chain reaction proper:

$$CH_4 + Cl\bullet \longrightarrow CH_3\bullet + HCl$$

$$CH_3\bullet + Cl_2 \longrightarrow CH_3Cl + Cl\bullet$$

charge cloud representation of atomic orbitals: *orbitals* represent the volume of space where an electron or electron pair exerts the property of 'electronness'; that is, the ability to overlap with other orbitals to form covalent bonds.

TIP Don't worry too much about what orbitals mean in terms of the wave model for the electron; for the purposes of the chemist they define where bonds can form.

charge density: the ratio of the charge on an ion to its surface area, though often loosely regarded as the ratio of charge to size.

Small ions with high charge have high charge density, which means there is a strong electrostatic field around them. They have high hydration energies and are polarising, leading to deviations from the *ionic model of crystal lattice* in their compounds.

e.g. Alkali metals have the lowest charge density in their period; ions such as Be^{2+} and Al^{3+} have high charge densities and many of their nominally ionic compounds have a high degree of covalent character.

chemiluminescence: the production of light instead of heat during the oxidation of some organic molecules.

e.g. The glow of fireflies or glow-worms results from a chemiluminescent reaction, and the slow oxidation of phosphorus, which emits a greenish light, is also such a reaction. Sugar crystals emit red flashes when crushed, but you need dark-adapted eyes to see this. Self-seal envelopes do the same on opening.

chiral centre: an atom, usually carbon, though it can be another element that forms covalent bonds, surrounded by four different atoms or groups of atoms.

- If a molecule has only one chiral centre (left-hand structure), it and its mirror image are non-superimposable and the molecule will be optically active. Molecules with two chiral centres may not be optically active (right-hand structure). (See also *chiral molecule; optical activity.*)

CH_3 CH_3CH_2 H OH H_3C OH H H_3C OH H

chiral molecule: a molecule that is non-superimposable on its mirror image.

- Such molecules are optically active. The molecule may have one or more *chiral centre*, or it may have none but be chiral because of some other feature, such as being helical. If a molecule has two chiral centres and one is the mirror-image of the other, the molecule as a whole is not chiral (structure above right). (See also *optical activity.*)

chromatography: literally 'colour writing', a name given to a variety of techniques where substances are separated according to differential *solubility* in two phases, one moving and one stationary.

- ***e.g.*** There are many chromatography techniques, including the use of paper, thin layers of cellulose, alumina or silica (in columns for large quantities), and *ion-exchange* resins, all with liquids as the moving phase (solvent or eluant); and silicone-oil-coated silica with an inert gas such as nitrogen or argon as the moving phase in gas–liquid chromatography.
- ***TIP*** Despite the name, the compounds need not be coloured.

***cis–trans* isomerism:** a variety of *isomerism* that arises in organic compounds because of restricted rotation about C=C bonds.

- Provided the groups on a given C=C carbon are not the same, there are then two arrangements possible: the *cis* and the *trans* isomers. The cis isomer has the functional groups on the same side of the double bond.
- ***e.g.*** The *cis* and *trans* isomers of 1,2-dichloroethene are shown below.

Cl Cl C=C H H   H Cl C=C Cl H

- ***TIP*** The restricted rotation is best visualised by remembering that the *p*-orbitals giving the double bond overlap sideways. The bond will rotate if the

temperature is raised sufficiently. The definition of *cis*- and *trans*- gives rise to difficulties with compounds like

$$\begin{array}{ccc} H & & CH_3 \\ & C{=}C & \\ CH_3CH_2CH_2 & & CH_2CH_3 \end{array}$$

where it has to be decided which groups are to be considered for the *cis*- or *trans*- label.

collision theory: the idea that reaction rates are explicable by considering the frequency and the energy of molecular collisions during the *rate-determining step* of a reaction.

■ ***TIP*** The collision energy, described by the *Maxwell–Boltzmann distribution*, is by far the more important of the two factors.

colorimeter: a device used for measuring the *concentration* of coloured substances in solution by passing visible light through the solution.

■ The wavelength of the light is determined by suitable filters, and the intensity of the transmitted light is measured. The colorimeter is calibrated by using solutions of known concentration.

combustion: rapid burning, usually in oxygen, to give heat and a flame.

■ Some substances will burn in other oxidising agents, particularly in fluorine and chlorine.

complex ion: an ion formed when a transition metal ion (or one of a number of non-transition metal ions) accepts pairs of electrons into vacant *orbitals* from donor molecules such as water or ammonia.

■ ***e.g.*** Copper accepts electrons from six water molecules to form $[Cu(H_2O)_6]^{2+}$; aqua complexes such as this are formed by all the *d*-block elements, as well as by metals in groups 2 and 3.

■ ***TIP*** The transition metals do not necessarily use their 3*d*-orbitals to accept the electrons — the 4*s*/*p*/*d* can be used too.

concentrated solution: a solution that contains a relatively large amount of *solute* compared with the amount of *solvent*; these amounts are not precisely defined.

■ ***e.g.*** Concentrated sulphuric acid is about 18 mol dm^{-3}; concentrated hydrochloric and nitric acids are about 11 mol dm^{-3}.

concentration: the amount of substance per unit volume of *solution*, measured in mol dm^{-3}.

■ This is often called the molarity of the solution. Concentrations are also measured in g dm^{-3} for convenience in weighing.

■ ***TIP*** The 'dm^{-3}' refers to the volume of the solution, not the volume of the added solvent.

condensation: the phase change from gas to liquid, or from gas to solid.

condensation polymerisation: the reaction between two different types of molecule to give a *polymer* accompanied by the loss of a small molecule such as water or hydrogen chloride.

e.g. The production of nylon-6,6 from hexamethylene diamine and adipoyl chloride:

$$\cdots\text{–}CH_2NH_2\ ClOC(CH_2)_4COCl\ H_2N(CH_2)_6NH_2\ ClOC(CH_2)_4COCl\ H_2NCH_2\text{–}\cdots$$

$$\downarrow$$

$$\cdots\text{–}CH_2NOC(CH_2)_4COHN(CH_2)_6NHOC(CH_2)_4COHNCH_2\text{–}\cdots$$

$$HCl \quad HCl \quad HCl \quad HCl$$

condensation reaction: a reaction between two molecules involving their addition together with the *elimination* of a small molecule such as water or hydrogen chloride.

e.g. The reaction of excess ethanol with concentrated sulphuric acid at 140°C to give ethoxyethane:

$$CH_3CH_2OH + HOCH_2CH_3 \longrightarrow CH_3CH_2OCH_2CH_3 + H_2O$$

conjugate acid–base pairs: these are formed when an *acid* dissociates.

The anion of an acid is a base by definition, and is the conjugate base of the acid. For an acid HA:

$HA(aq)$	+	$H_2O(l)$	$\longrightarrow$	$H_3O^+(aq)$	+	$A^-(aq)$
acid		base		conjugate acid		conjugate base

e.g.

$HCl(aq)$	+	$H_2O(l)$	$\longrightarrow$	$H_3O^+(aq)$	+	$Cl^-(aq)$
acid (strong)		base		conjugate acid		conjugate base (weak)
$H_2SO_3(aq)$	+	$H_2O(l)$	$\longrightarrow$	$H_3O^+(aq)$	+	$HSO_3^-(aq)$
acid (weak)		base		conjugate acid		conjugate base (strong)

TIP When showing the pairs in an equation it is helpful to join them with a line to avoid any ambiguity.

H_2SO_4	+	H_2O	$\longrightarrow$	H_2O^+	+	HSO_4^-
acid		base		conjugate acid		conjugate base

contact process: the oxidation of sulphur dioxide with oxygen using a vanadium(V) oxide *catalyst*.

The SO_3 produced is absorbed in concentrated sulphuric acid, which is then diluted with water to the required *concentration*. Direct reaction of sulphur trioxide with water is too violent.

coordination number: the number of nearest neighbours an atom or ion has in a crystal structure, or the number of other atoms or groups bonded to a given atom in a covalent compound.

e.g. Many metals are hexagonally close-packed structures in which each atom has 12 nearest neighbours, so 12 is therefore the coordination number.

In CCl_4 the carbon atom is bonded to four other atoms, so it has a coordination number of 4.

corrosion: the process by which a metal undergoes *oxidation* by water and air.

■ Corrosion is exacerbated where two metals join or where there are surface cracks in the metal due to working it.

■ ***TIP*** Only iron can rust; for all other metals 'corrosion' or 'oxidation' is the correct term.

coupling reaction: a reaction between a *diazonium compound* and a *phenol* in alkaline solution; the product is an *azo dye*.

■ ***e.g.*** The reaction between benzenediazonium chloride and 2-naphthol gives a red solid, phenylazo-2-naphthol:

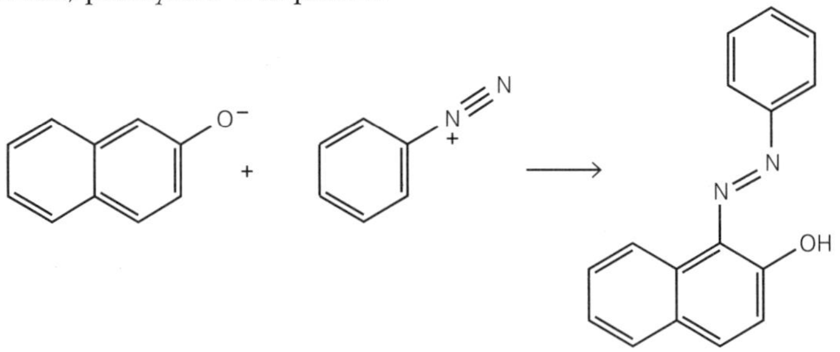

covalent bond: a bond formed by the overlap of atomic *orbitals* such that the electron density between the atoms comes from two electrons.

covalent radius: half the inter-nuclear distance between two identical covalently bonded atoms.

■ Tables of covalent radii can be used to find the length of covalent bonds between different atoms and give good results unless one of the atoms is very electronegative.

cryolite: sodium aluminium fluoride, Na_3AlF_6.

■ This is used as the *solvent* in the *Hall–Héroult cell* for the *electrolysis* of alumina to give aluminium. The electrolyte is about 90% cryolite, 5% aluminium oxide and 5% calcium fluoride. All cryolite used is synthetic.

curly arrow: an arrow used to show the movement of a pair of electrons in a *reaction mechanism*.

■ The tail of the arrow shows where the electrons come from, the head where they go to.

■ ***e.g.*** See S_N1 and S_N2 for examples of the use of curly arrows.

■ ***TIP*** Do not bring arrows to or from charges. The arrowhead can go either to the attacked atom, or halfway between the attacking and the attacked, to the midpoint of where the bond will be.

cycloalkane (also called 'alicyclic compound')**:** a ring compound with the general formula C_nH_{2n}, where n is 3 or greater.

e.g. The compounds cyclopropane, C_3H_6, to cyclooctane, C_8H_{16}, are shown as their conventional *skeletal formulae* below.

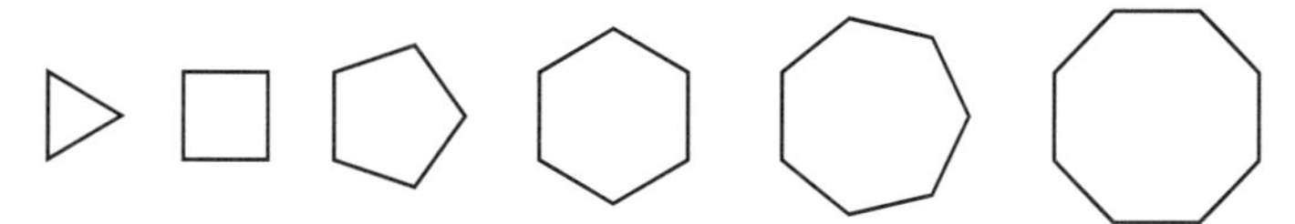

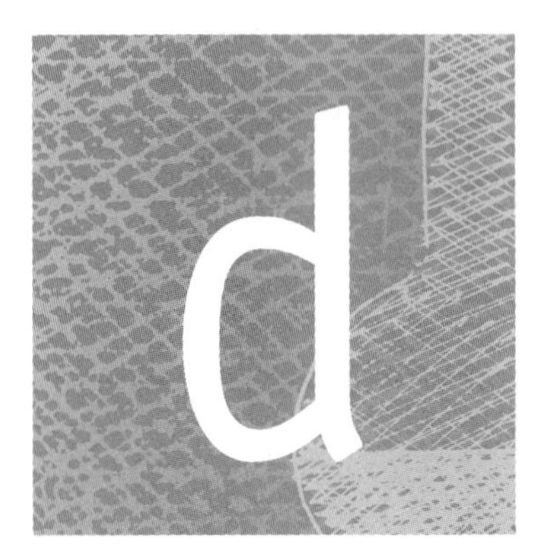

Daniell cell: the *electrochemical cell* whose conventional representation is:

$Zn \mid Zn^{2+}(aq) \parallel Cu^{2+}(aq) \mid Cu$

■ It has a standard cell potential of 1.10 V, which is nearly independent of temperature. It is named after J. F. Daniell, who made the first cell of this type.

dative covalent bond: a covalent bond where both electrons come from one of the atoms.

■ Such bonds are sometimes shown with an arrow representing the bond, as in the complex $H_3N \longrightarrow BF_3$, but they are actually no different from any other covalent bond.

***d*-block element:** metal elements where the *d*-shell is being filled across the *period*; that is, the elements 21–30, 39–48, 57, 72–80, 89 and 104–112.

■ ***e.g.*** The first-row elements are from $_{21}Sc$ to $_{30}Zn$.

***d–d* transition:** an *electronic transition* between two *d*-orbitals.

■ Such transitions are responsible for the colour of many *transition element* ions. These transitions are 'forbidden' according to quantum theory, that is they have an extremely low probability. The colours are therefore not very intense.

■ ***e.g.*** The blue colour of $[Cu(H_2O)_6]^{2+}$ is due to *d–d* transitions absorbing red light. Copper(I), which has the electron structure $[Ar]3d^{10}$, has no spaces for the electrons to move, and is therefore not coloured.

■ ***TIP*** Ions that have the transition element in an oxidation state that leaves it with no *d*-electrons, for example MnO_4^- or $Cr_2O_7^{2-}$, are coloured for different reasons and their colours are much more intense.

dehydrating agent: a substance that removes water or the elements of water from a compound (*see dehydration*).

dehydration: either the loss of water from a compound or the loss of the elements of water from a compound.

■ The compound does not necessarily contain water itself, but could lose hydrogen and oxygen in the ratio of 2 to 1.

■ ***e.g.*** Concentrated sulphuric acid will dehydrate sucrose to carbon:

$$C_{12}H_{22}O_{11} \longrightarrow 12C + 11H_2O$$

This is a strongly *exothermic reaction* owing to the ionisation of the sulphuric acid and the hydration of these ions. Phosphorus(v) oxide dehydrates concentrated sulphuric acid to sulphur trioxide, and is therefore a better dehydrating agent than sulphuric acid:

$$6H_2SO_4 + P_4O_{10} \longrightarrow 4H_3PO_4 + 6SO_3$$

TIP The water may be present as such, e.g. *water of crystallisation*, or the compound may lose two hydrogens for each oxygen, as in the case of sucrose dehydration, shown above.

deliquescence: the property shown by some salts of absorbing enough water vapour from the atmosphere to form a solution.

e.g. Calcium chloride, $CaCl_2$, on standing in air forms a pool of saturated solution.

delocalisation of electrons: molecules that have *p-orbitals* extending over several atom centres have delocalised electrons.

This usually results in lower *enthalpies of hydrogenation* than for the equivalent non-delocalised system.

e.g. The enthalpy of hydrogenation of benzene, which has a delocalised system, is -208 kJ mol^{-1}; that of cyclohexa-1,3,5-triene, the compound with three non-delocalised double bonds, is estimated at about -360 kJ mol^{-1}.

deprotonation: the loss of a *proton*, usually applied to the effect of *hydroxide ions* on hydrated *complex ions*.

e.g. $[Cu(H_2O)_6]^{2+} + OH^- \longrightarrow [Cu(H_2O)_5(OH)]^+ + H_2O$

$[Al(H_2O)_6]^{3+}(aq) + H_2O(l) \longrightarrow [Al(H_2O)_5(OH)]^{2+}(aq) + H_3O^+(aq)$

desiccant: a material used for drying, usually in a *desiccator*.

e.g. Anhydrous calcium chloride, silica gel and phosphorus(v) oxide are all common desiccants.

TIP Note the spelling: one 's', two 'c's.

desiccator: a device for drying crystals.

The wet crystals are placed on a gauze over a suitable drying agent, such as calcium chloride or phosphorus(v) oxide. In a vacuum desiccator the air is then pumped out. The water vaporises and then reacts with the desiccant. Desiccators are made from glass.

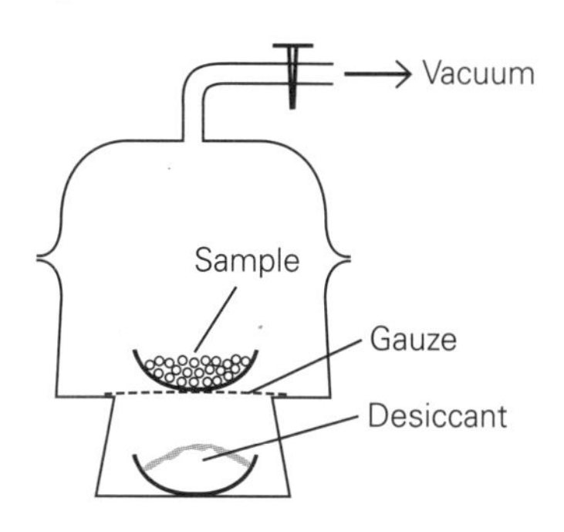

detergent: water-soluble mixtures that can emulsify grease and with this action remove dirt.

■ There are many synthetic detergents; they are used for washing fabrics, surfaces, and so on, and contain a *surface active agent* together with other ingredients, such as bleaches or whiteness enhancers.

deuterium: the isotope of hydrogen having a neutron in the nucleus and therefore a relative atomic mass of 2; it is often given the symbol D in formulae.

Devarda's alloy: an alloy used in alkaline solution to reduce nitrates to ammonia in qualitative analysis.

■ It is 45% aluminium, 5% zinc and 50% copper.

diamond: an allotrope of carbon which has layers of chair-shaped six-membered rings and covalent bonds throughout, with every carbon atom joined tetrahedrally to four others.

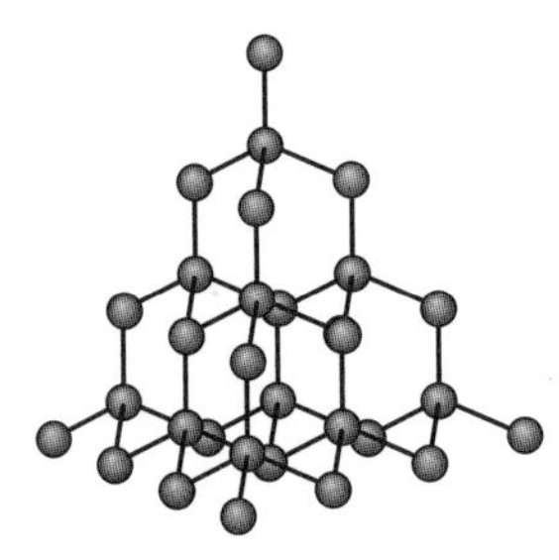

■ It is the hardest substance known.

diaphragm cell: an electrolytic cell for the production of sodium hydroxide, hydrogen and chlorine from sodium chloride solution or brine.

■ The *anode* and *cathode* compartments are separated by a porous diaphragm of asbestos. The diaphragm cell is being replaced by the *membrane cell*, which has an ion-selective membrane in place of the diaphragm; this gives a purer sodium hydroxide product.

diatomic molecule: a molecule made from two atoms.

■ ***e.g.*** H_2, Cl_2, HCl.

diazonium compound: an important intermediate in the manufacture of *azo dyes*, formed by *diazotisation*.

■ Diazonium compounds are of the form $ArN_2^+X^-$.

diazotisation: the reaction of sodium nitrite with a primary aromatic amine in the presence of concentrated hydrochloric acid, at 0–5°C.

■ The diazonium salt produced is used immediately and not isolated.

■ ***e.g.*** Benzenediazonium chloride:

$\overset{+}{N}\equiv N$

Cl^-

■ ***TIP*** If the temperature goes below 0°C, the reaction is too slow; much above 5°C and the product begins to decompose.

dibasic acid: an acid that has two replaceable hydrogen atoms per molecule.

■ These acids often give two sorts of salt.

■ ***e.g.*** Sulphuric acid, H_2SO_4; this forms two series of salts, e.g. sodium hydrogen sulphate, $NaHSO_4$, and sodium sulphate, Na_2SO_4.

dicarboxylic acid: an organic acid containing two –COOH groups.

■ ***e.g.*** The simplest is ethanedioic acid, HOOC–COOH.

diesel: a fuel oil for diesel engines with a volatility and viscosity intermediate between paraffin (kerosene) and lubricating oil.

diffusion: the movement of a *gas* (in a gaseous mixture) or a *solute* (in a solution) from an area of high concentration to one of low concentration until its distribution is uniform.

dilute solution: a rather vague term that indicates a relatively small amount of *solute* per unit volume of *solution*.

■ Dilute solutions of ordinary laboratory reagents usually have a *concentration* of 1–2 mol dm^{-3}.

2,4-dinitrophenylhydrazine: *see Brady's reagent.*

dipole–dipole forces: electrostatic intermolecular forces between permanent or temporary dipoles; known generically as *van der Waals forces*.

dispersion forces: *intermolecular forces* that arise because of movement of electrons within molecules giving rise to temporary dipoles.

■ They are part of the set of intermolecular forces known as *van der Waals forces*.

■ ***TIP*** They are called dispersion forces because they are involved in the dispersion of light by a transparent substance.

displacement reaction: a *redox reaction* in which a reactive metal reduces the ions of a less reactive metal, often but not necessarily in solution.

■ ***e.g.*** In solution: $Cu^{2+}(aq) + Fe(s) \longrightarrow Cu(s) + Fe^{2+}(aq)$.

Between solids: $Fe_2O_3(s) + 2Al(s) \longrightarrow Al_2O_3(s) + 2Fe(l)$ (the Thermit reaction).

■ ***TIP*** Displacement reactions are of limited use in determining relative reactivity as many of these reactions are slow, even though thermodynamically feasible.

disproportionation: a reaction where a given element (which may be present as the element, in a compound or in an ion) simultaneously undergoes *oxidation* and *reduction*.

■ ***e.g.*** chlorine disproportionates in *aqueous solution*; the oxidation state of the chlorine in each case is shown:

$$\underset{(0)}{Cl_2(aq)} + H_2O(l) \longrightarrow \underset{(+1)}{HOCl(aq)} + \underset{(-1)}{HCl(aq)}$$

■ ***TIP*** The element concerned must have at least three *oxidation states* and be in an intermediate state. Show the disproportionation by putting in the oxidation states as shown above.

dissociation: the splitting of a molecule into two or more smaller fragments, which could be atoms, molecules, *ions* or *radicals*.

■ ***e.g.*** To atoms (and radicals): $Cl_2 \longrightarrow 2Cl\bullet$

To molecules: $N_2O_4 \rightleftharpoons 2NO_2$

To ions: $H_2SO_4 \longrightarrow H^+ + HSO_4^-$

distillation: the process of vaporising a liquid and then cooling the vapour to liquefy it.

■ Used to separate liquids from non-volatile impurities. Mixtures of volatile liquids are separated by fractional distillation.

***d*-orbitals:** *orbitals* found for the first time in the third *quantum shell*; there are five of these orbitals, so they can be up to 10 electrons.

■ ***TIP*** The phrase 'can be up to 10 electrons' is used because the orbitals are not boxes into which the electrons are placed. The orbital is the electron(s), up to two for each.

double decomposition: see *precipitation reaction*.

double salt: a salt containing two or more individual salts that has distinct properties as a solid but behaves as a mixture of the salts when in solution.

■ ***e.g.*** ammonium iron(II) sulphate is made by crystallising a solution equimolar in ammonium sulphate and iron(II) sulphate. It is a pale green hydrated solid, $(NH_4)_2SO_4.FeSO_4.7H_2O$. The wide variety of alums (which do not necessarily contain aluminium) are also double salts: two such are potassium alum, $K_2SO_4.Al_2(SO_4)_3.24H_2O$, and chrome alum $Cr_2(SO_4)_3.K_2SO_4.24H_2O$.

dye: a brightly coloured compound used to colour fabrics by binding on to the surface of the material.

■ Until the invention of the aniline dyes by William Perkin in the 1880s, the only bright dye was Tyrian purple. Produced from whelks at enormous expense, it became, for this reason, the colour favoured by emperors and royalty.

■ ***e.g.*** The dye mauveine was first used to print the twopenny purple stamp of 1883.

dynamic equilibrium: a reaction where the forward and reverse reactions both occur at the same rate, so that although many molecules are reacting, there is no overall change in the *concentration* of any of them.

■ ***e.g.*** Esterification:

$$CH_3COOH + CH_3CH_2OH \rightleftharpoons CH_3COOCH_2CH_3 + H_2O$$

efflorescence: the process where *water of crystallisation* is lost by a hydrated salt.

■ ***e.g.*** Sodium carbonate decahydrate, $Na_2CO_3.10H_2O$, gradually loses water on standing in air.

electrochemical cell: an arrangement of two electrodes dipping into electrolyte solutions that generates an e.m.f.

■ ***e.g.*** The *Daniell cell* was one of the earliest; consisting of a copper electrode and a zinc electrode joined by a *salt bridge*, its conventional representation is:

$Zn \mid Zn^{2+}(aq) \parallel Cu^{2+}(aq) \mid Cu$

The single vertical line | shows a boundary between solid and solution, the double vertical line || shows the salt bridge.

■ ***TIP*** The first battery was made from alternate plates of copper and zinc separated by cloth soaked in brine. Strictly speaking, a battery is several cells joined in series. The popular AA 1.5 V 'battery' is actually a cell.

electrochemical series: the elements arranged in order of their standard *reduction potentials*, with the most negative at the top of the series.

■ Ions such as MnO_4^- and compounds such as MnO_2, which can undergo *redox reactions*, are also included.

■ ***TIP*** The position of an element or ion in the electrochemical series does not indicate the speed of reaction. The electrochemical series is a *thermodynamic*, not a *kinetic*, idea.

electrochemistry: the study of *electrolysis*, *electrochemical cells* and the properties of ionic solutions.

electrode: metal or graphite introduced into an *electrolyte* to enable electron transfer. Electrodes may be inert, functioning only to transfer electrons, or may be active and involved in the cell reactions.

■ ***e.g.*** The electrodes used in the *diaphragm cell* for the production of sodium hydroxide do not enter into the reactions producing hydrogen and chlorine. However, the impure copper anode used in the purification of copper disappears as electrolysis proceeds owing to the reaction

$Cu(s) \longrightarrow Cu^{2+}(aq) + 2e^-$

electrode potential: the potential, measured relative to some stated electrode, formed between a metal and a solution of its ions or between ions of the same element in different *oxidation states*.

- The *standard electrode potential* is measured relative to the standard hydrogen electrode, whose potential is defined as 0.00 V, with all concentrations at 1 mol dm^{-3}.
- **e.g.** A piece of copper dipping in a solution of copper sulphate of concentration 1 mol dm^{-3} and at pH 0, and connected to a standard hydrogen electrode, gives a cell with a potential of + 0.34 V — this is the electrode potential of the Cu^{2+}/Cu system.

electrolysis: the decomposition of an *electrolyte* by the passage of current.

- Many electrolytes are molten salts or aqueous salt solutions.
- **e.g.** Molten sodium chloride is electrolysed to give sodium and chlorine. Sodium chloride solution in the *diaphragm cell* gives sodium hydroxide, chlorine and hydrogen.
- ***TIP*** The conduction in the melt or the solution is by ions: no electrons pass between the electrodes.

electrolyte: the liquid in an electrolytic cell or an *electrochemical cell*.

- In the case of the electrolytic cell, it is the electrolyte that is decomposed by *electrolysis*. In an electrochemical cell the electrolyte concentrations will change as the cell discharges. This change is sometimes reversible, as in the *lead–acid battery*.
- **e.g.** The following are significant:

Cell	Electrolyte	Electrodes	Product(s)
Electrolytic cells			
Downs cell	Molten sodium chloride		Sodium and chlorine
Hall–Héroult cell	Alumina dissolved in molten cryolite	Graphite	Aluminium
Diaphragm cell	Aqueous sodium chloride		Sodium hydroxide, hydrogen and chlorine
Copper refining	Copper sulphate solution	Copper	Pure copper from impure copper
Electrochemical cells			
Lead–acid battery	Sulphuric acid	Lead and lead(IV) oxide	Electricity
Nickel–cadmium cell	Sodium hydroxide solution	Nickel and cadmium coated with their hydroxides	Electricity
Zinc–carbon 'dry' cell or Leclanche cell	Paste of ammonium chloride	Zinc and carbon	Electricity

electron: the fundamental entity having a charge of -1.6×10^{-19} C and a mass of 9.11×10^{-31} kg (this is 1/1836 the mass of a proton).

- Chemistry is the story of electron interactions.

electron affinity: the *enthalpy change* accompanying the gain of electrons in the gas phase.

- The first electron affinity for the element X is the enthalpy change per mole for the process

$$X(g) + e^- \longrightarrow X^-(g)$$

The second electron affinity is the enthalpy change per mole for the process

$$X^-(g) + e^- \longrightarrow X^{2-}(g)$$

electron configuration: the arrangement of the electrons in an atom according to the *aufbau principle*.

electron-deficient compound: compound where some atoms do not have filled shells.

- ***e.g.*** Boron trifluoride, BF_3, has six electrons around the boron atom.

electronegativity: the tendency of an atom in a *covalent bond* to attract electrons.

- Electronegativity differences give an idea of the *polarity* of the bond. Electronegativity values increase from left to right in the periodic table and decrease going down a group.
- ***TIP*** There are various electronegativity scales, that due to Linus Pauling being the commonest. The electronegativity is a property of an atom in a molecule — it is not a property of the atom itself. It is to some extent dependent on the oxidation state of the element; lead(II) is 1.8, lead(IV) is 2.0.

electronic transition: the movement of electrons from one *orbital* to another.

- The movement is either to an orbital of higher energy by absorption of energy, or to one of lower energy with the emission of radiation.
- ***e.g.*** Transitions from lower to higher energy give the colour to *transition element* ions (*d–d transitions*), those from higher to lower energy give the emission spectra of elements in, for example, the *flame test*.

electrons-in-boxes notation: a notation system in which atomic *orbitals* are regarded as boxes into which electrons are placed.

- ***e.g.*** Sodium, which has the electronic configuration $1s^22s^22p^63s^1$, can also be represented as

1*s*	2*s*	2*p*			3*s*
↑↓	↑↓	↑↓	↑↓	↑↓	↑

- ***TIP*** Remember that orbitals are not boxes into which electrons are placed; the orbitals are the electrons.

electron transfer reaction: another name for a *redox* reaction, which is shorthand for oxidation–reduction reaction.

electrophile: a species that seeks out areas of high electron density when it reacts.

e.g. Bromine and the nitronium ion, NO_2^+, are common electrophilic reagents.

electrophilic addition: the reaction of an *electrophile* which adds across a C=C bond to give an addition product.

e.g. Bromine reacts with ethene at room temperature to give 1,2-dibromo-ethane:

$$CH_2{=}CH_2 + Br_2 \longrightarrow BrCH_2CH_2Br$$

The electrophile is $Br^{\delta+}$ formed by polarisation of the bromine molecule by the high electron density in the double bond.

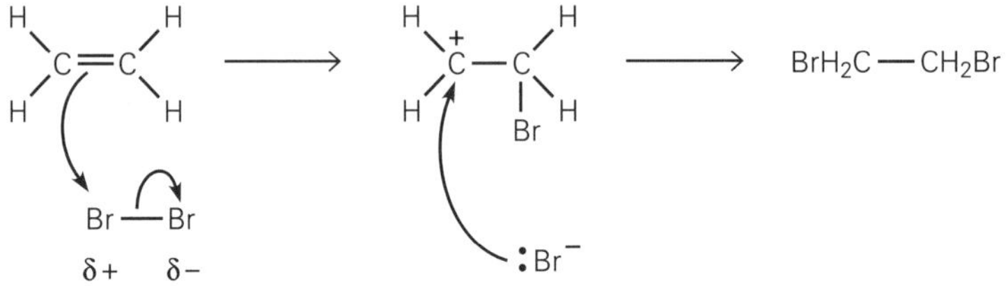

$$H_2C{=}CH_2 + \overset{\delta+}{Br}{-}\overset{\delta-}{Br} \longrightarrow H_2\overset{+}{C}{-}CH_2Br + {:}Br^- \longrightarrow BrH_2C{-}CH_2Br$$

electrophilic substitution: a reaction whereby an *electrophile* substitutes for another atom or group on the molecule.

e.g. In the *nitration* of benzene

$$C_6H_6 + HNO_3 \longrightarrow C_6H_5NO_2 + H_2O$$

the electrophile NO_2^+ is generated in *nitrating mixture* by the reaction

$$2H_2SO_4 + HNO_3 \longrightarrow NO_2^+ + H_3O^+ + 2HSO_4^-$$

and substitutes a hydrogen atom.

element: a substance containing only one type of atom, all with the same number of protons in the nucleus.

elementary particle: originally this meant the proton, neutron and electron, but the number of such particles is now rather large and the definition is perhaps less useful than once it was.

elimination: a reaction where a small molecule is lost either from within a single molecule, usually to give a double bond, or between two molecules.

e.g. 1-bromobutane and ethanolic potassium hydroxide solution gives but-1-ene as the main organic product, HBr having been eliminated:

$$CH_3CH_2CH_2CH_2Br + KOH \longrightarrow CH_3CH_2CH{=}CH_2 + KBr + H_2O$$

If ethanol is warmed at 140°C in excess with concentrated sulphuric acid, elimination of water occurs between two molecules to give ethoxyethane:

$$CH_3CH_2OH + HOCH_2CH_3 \longrightarrow CH_3CH_2OCH_2CH_3 + H_2O$$

TIP Potassium hydroxide is used rather than sodium hydroxide in the first reaction quoted because it is more soluble in alcohol. Other reactions occur to produce butan-1-ol and butoxybutane.

elution: the process of running a solvent down a column in *chromatography* to obtain the separate fractions.

The solvent is called the eluant, the product solution the eluate.

empirical formula: the formula of a compound expressed in its lowest whole-number ratio.

- It is the composition that is obtained by experiment.
- ***e.g.*** The empirical formula for benzene (C_6H_6), cyclobutadiene (C_4H_4) and ethyne (C_2H_2) is CH.

emulsifying agent: a compound that enables an *emulsion* to be stable over long periods of time.

- Emulsifying agents are *surface active agents.*
- ***e.g.*** Soaps, detergents, lecithin.

emulsion: a suspension of one *liquid* in fine droplets in another liquid with which it is immiscible.

- ***e.g.*** Emulsion paint, mayonnaise.
- ***TIP*** For the emulsion to be stable, an *emulsifying agent* is necessary, otherwise the droplets of liquid will coalesce and the mixture will separate into two phases. In mayonnaise it is the lecithin in egg yolk.

enantiomer: the non-superimposable mirror image of a *chiral molecule.*

- ***e.g.*** The enantiomers of the amino acid alanine are:

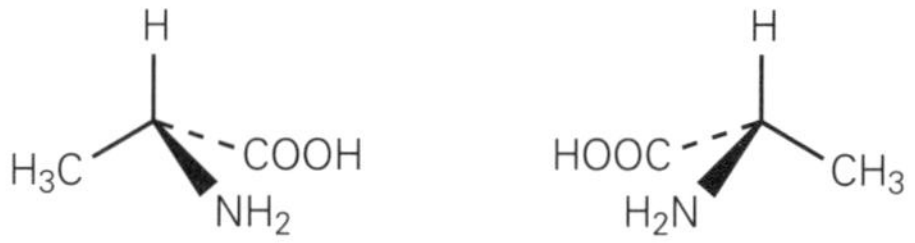

H H

H_3C COOH HOOC CH_3

NH_2 H_2N

endothermic reaction: a reaction that takes in heat from the surroundings.

- ***e.g.*** The reaction of nitrogen with oxygen to give nitrogen monoxide is endothermic:

$$N_2 + O_2 \longrightarrow 2NO \qquad \Delta H = +180.4\ \text{kJ mol}^{-1}$$

- ***TIP*** Always include the + sign in any statement of endothermic enthalpy changes.

end point: the point during a *titration* when the indicator changes colour suddenly.

enthalpy change: the heat change accompanying a reaction at constant pressure.

- It is represented as ΔH and conventionally is negative if heat is given out to the surroundings.
- ***TIP*** Heat changes at constant volume are different if there is a volume change accompanying the reaction. Most chemistry is done in open vessels, i.e. at constant pressure, so enthalpy change values are most used. A note concerning the enthalpy changes on the next two pages. All can be converted into 'standard enthalpy of...' by adding 'all substances being in their standard states at specified temperature'. The specified temperature is 298 K unless otherwise stated. This temperature is not part of the original definition but is becoming understood by common usage.

enthalpy level diagram: a diagram that shows the relative enthalpy levels of reactants and products.

- Only relative values can be measured — the absolute value of the enthalpy of a system cannot. Enthalpy level diagrams often include a pathway to show the energy levels during a reaction. The horizontal axis may be regarded as time — really it relates to the progress of the reaction.
- **e.g.** The reaction of a methyl *radical* with HCl shows the following energy changes:

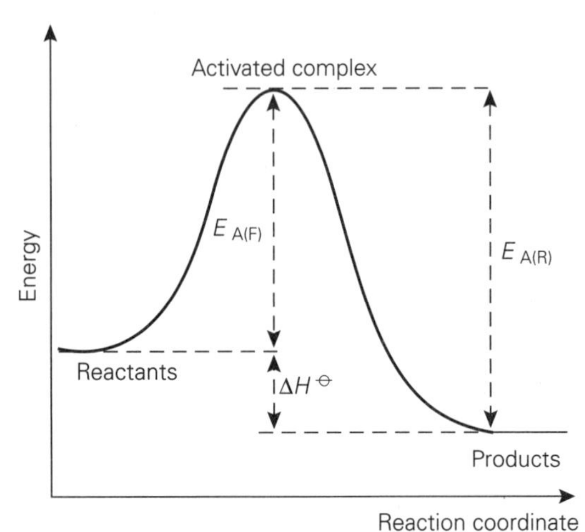

enthalpy of atomisation, ΔH_a: the heat change accompanying the formation of one mole of atoms of an element in the gas phase at constant pressure:

$$E(s) \longrightarrow E(g) \text{ or } \tfrac{1}{2}E_2(g) \longrightarrow E(g)$$

depending on the original form of the element.

- **e.g.** $\tfrac{1}{2}Cl_2(g) \longrightarrow Cl\ (g) \qquad \Delta H_a = +121\ kJ\ mol^{-1}$
- ***TIP*** The heat change is for formation of a mole of atoms, not for the use of a mole of the element to begin with. This latter belief is the commonest error in using ΔH_a.

enthalpy of combustion, ΔH_c: the heat change at constant pressure when one mole of substance is burnt in excess oxygen. All enthalpies of combustion are negative.

- **e.g.** $CH_4(g) + 2O_2(g) \longrightarrow CO_2(g) + 2H_2O(l) \qquad \Delta H_c = -890.4\ kJ\ mol^{-1}$
- ***TIP*** This value would be different (less exothermic) if the product water were gaseous.

enthalpy of formation, ΔH_f: the heat change at constant pressure when one mole of substance is formed from its elements.

- **e.g.** $2C(graphite) + 3H_2(g) \longrightarrow C_2H_6(g) \qquad \Delta H_f = -84.7\ kJ\ mol^{-1}$
- ***TIP*** Note that 'its elements' is not the same as 'atoms'. In the case of elements capable of *allotropy*, the allotrope used must be specified. Enthalpies of formation do not necessarily refer to reactions that can actually occur. The reaction shown above is an example: you cannot make ethane from carbon

and hydrogen directly. Many heats of formation are necessarily obtained from other thermochemical measurements by using *Hess's law*.

enthalpy of hydration, ΔH_{hyd}: the heat change at constant pressure when one mole of ions in the gas phase is dissolved in water to give a solution so dilute that addition of further solvent causes no further heat change.

- The water is shown as 'aq' in equations. All enthalpies of hydration are negative.
- ***e.g.*** $Na^+(g) + aq \longrightarrow Na^+(aq)$ $\Delta H_{hyd} = -406\ kJ\ mol^{-1}$
  $Mg^{2+}(g) + aq \longrightarrow Mg^{2+}(aq)$ $\Delta H_{hyd} = -1920\ kJ\ mol^{-1}$
- ***TIP*** The smaller the ion and the larger its charge, i.e. the higher its *charge density*, the more exothermic its ΔH_{hyd}.

enthalpy of hydrogenation: the enthalpy change for the addition of hydrogen across a multiple bond.

- ***e.g.*** the enthalpy of hydrogenation of ethene to give ethane is 126 kJ mol^{-1}:
  $H_2C{=}CH_2 + H_2 \longrightarrow CH_3CH_3$

enthalpy of neutralisation, ΔH_{neut}: the heat change at constant pressure when one mole of water is formed by the reaction of an acid with a base in aqueous solution:

$H^+(aq) + OH^-(aq) \longrightarrow H_2O(l)$

- ***e.g.*** For strong acids and strong bases, ΔH_{neut} is around $-57\ kJ\ mol^{-1}$. Weak acids give less exothermic values. For HCN reacting with NaOH, ΔH_{neut} is $-11.7\ kJ\ mol^{-1}$.
- ***TIP*** The value is for the formation of one mole of water, not for the use of one mole of acid.

enthalpy of solution, ΔH_{soln}: the heat change at constant pressure when one mole of substance is dissolved in water to make a *solution* sufficiently dilute that further addition of *solvent* causes no further heat change.

- The water is shown as '(aq)' in equations.
- ***e.g.*** $NaCl(s) + aq \longrightarrow Na^+(aq) + Cl^-(aq)$ $\Delta H_{soln} = +\ 3.9\ kJ\ mol^{-1}$

entropy: in classical thermodynamics, entropy is the quantity dq/T, where q is the heat absorbed by a system at temperature T; in modern chemistry, it is associated with the disorder or randomness of a system — the more random a system becomes, the higher its entropy.

- ***TIP*** Entropy is one of the most important ideas in the whole of chemistry; it is the only physical quantity that defines the direction of time. The feasibility of a chemical reaction is given by the equation

  $\Delta G = \Delta H - T\Delta S$

  where the quantity ΔG, the Gibbs function or the Gibbs free energy change, is negative for any *spontaneous chemical change*. Some processes are dominated by ΔH and are enthalpy controlled; others are dominated by ΔS and so are entropy controlled. Entropy is so important that you should find out about it even if it is not in any syllabus that you are studying.

enzyme: a *catalyst* for biochemical reactions.

Enzymes are proteins, and a given enzyme usually shows catalytic activity for only one reaction. They operate over a fairly narrow range of temperature and pH, which is also specific to the enzyme concerned.

e.g. Catalase is present in all animal cells, and catalyses the reaction

$$H_2O_2 \longrightarrow H_2O + {}^1/_2O_2$$

It is one of the most effective of all catalysts — *peroxides* damage cells, and have been implicated in ageing processes.

equilibrium: a short version of *dynamic equilibrium.*

equilibrium constant, K_c: for a reaction

$$aA + bB + \ldots \rightleftharpoons mM + nN + \ldots$$

the equilibrium constant at a given temperature is defined in terms of (a) *concentrations* (for substances in solution or in the gas phase) or (b) *partial pressures* (for substances in the gas phase).

(a) For substances in solution, the equilibrium constant in terms of concentrations is used:

$$K_c = \frac{[M]^m[N]^n\ldots}{[A]^a[B]^b\ldots}$$

where [X] is the equilibrium concentration in mol dm^{-3} of substance X. It can also be used for reactions in the gas phase.

(b) For substances in the gas phase, the equilibrium constant in terms of *partial pressures* is often used:

$$K_p = \frac{p(M)^m p(N)^n\ldots}{p(A)^a p(B)^b\ldots}$$

where $p(X)$ is the equilibrium partial pressure of the substance X.

e.g. (a) For the esterification reaction where all substances are liquids:

$$CH_3CH_2OH + CH_3COOH \rightleftharpoons CH_3COOCH_2CH_3 + H_2O$$

$$K_c = \frac{[CH_3COOCH_2CH_3][H_2O]}{[CH_3CH_2OH][CH_3COOH]}$$

(b) For the thermal decomposition of phosphorus pentachloride in the gas phase:

$$PCl_5 \rightleftharpoons PCl_3 + Cl_2$$

$$K_p = \frac{p(PCl_3)p(Cl_2)}{p(PCl_5)}$$

TIP The equilibrium constant depends on the form of the equation, and the two must always be written together. Do not use square brackets in expressions for K_p.

ester: usually used to mean a compound of the form RCOOR′, where R can be H, *aliphatic* or *aromatic*, and R′ can be aliphatic or aromatic.

There are also inorganic esters, such as alkyl hydrogen sulphates or phosphates. Organic esters often have pleasant smells and are widely used in the food and perfumery industries.

■ ***e.g.*** Ethyl ethanoate, $CH_3COOCH_2CH_3$, is an excellent *solvent* and is used in nail polish remover, as well as in much larger solvent applications in industry.

ether: a substance of the form R–O–R, where the R groups may be the same or different, *aliphatic* or *aromatic*.

■ Apart from combustion, ethers are unreactive and are excellent *solvents*.

■ ***e.g.*** The commonest ether, usually called just 'ether', is ethoxyethane, $CH_3CH_2OCH_2CH_3$. The main problem in using it is its low boiling temperature of around 30°C and the explosive nature of the easily formed air/vapour mixture.

ethyl: the group CH_3CH_2–.

■ It is often written C_2H_5–, as this is unambiguous, or (especially in more advanced texts) as Et–.

■ ***TIP*** Avoid Et– in examinations.

eutectic: a mixture of substances which nevertheless shows a sharp *melting temperature*, unlike most mixtures, which melt over a range of temperature.

■ ***TIP*** Welding rods for steel are often made from a eutectic alloy that freezes suddenly.

evaporation: the loss of *vapour* from the surface of a *liquid* at temperatures below its *boiling temperature*.

■ ***TIP*** The *Maxwell–Boltzmann distribution* suggests that some molecules in the surface of a liquid will have enough energy to break free from the surface. This is the reason for evaporation.

exothermic reaction: a reaction that gives out heat to the surroundings.

■ Most reactions are exothermic. The sign given to the value of the heat change is conventionally negative.

■ ***e.g.*** The burning of natural gas:

$$CH_4(g) + 2O_2(g) \longrightarrow CO_2(g) + 2H_2O(l) \qquad \Delta H_c = -890.4 \text{ kJ mol}^{-1}$$

■ ***TIP*** Always include the negative sign in any statement of exothermic enthalpy changes.

explosion: very fast combustion, accompanied by a large increase in temperature and volume, though explosion can occur in constant volume circumstances when there will be a large increase in the pressure.

exponential decay: the decay of radioactive nuclei, and the rate of change of *concentration* in a first-order chemical reaction.

■ It is characterised by a constant *half-life*, independent of the number of atoms initially present or of the initial concentration of the substance. In the case of radioactive decay, the process is described by

$$N = N_0 e^{-\lambda t}$$

where N_0 is the initial number of atoms at some arbitrary time, N is the number at time t, and λ is the decay constant. The form of the equation for a first-order chemical process is similar.

Fajan's rules: guidelines indicating the degree of covalence in a compound.

■ Increased covalence is favoured by:

- large charge on either cation or anion
- small cation
- large anion
- cation with non-inert gas electron structure

■ ***TIP*** The rules are helpful in making approximate comparisons between compounds.

faraday: the charge carried by a mole of electrons, that is 96 484 C.

■ This is the amount of charge required to discharge one mole of univalent ions in *electrolysis*, or half a mole of divalent ions, or one-third of a mole of trivalent ions.

■ ***e.g.*** In the electrolysis of molten sodium chloride the electrode reactions are:

$$Na^+ + e^- \longrightarrow Na \text{ and } Cl^- \longrightarrow {}^1/_2Cl_2 + e^-$$

One faraday of charge will therefore give 23 g of sodium (molar mass of sodium is 23 g mol^{-1}) and 35.5 g of chlorine (molar mass of chlorine is 71 g mol^{-1}).

■ ***TIP*** Faraday is the only scientist to have two units named after him; the other is the unit of capacitance, the farad.

fat: an *ester* of fatty acids with glycerol, propan-1,2,3-triol.

■ The esterifying acids may be all the same or may be different. They are solid or semi-solid; liquid fats are usually called oils. *Hydrolysis* of fats with sodium hydroxide solution gives *soaps.*

■ ***e.g.*** Tristearin is the glyceryl ester of stearic acid, $C_{17}H_{35}COOH$:

$$\begin{array}{l} C_{17}H_{35}COOCH_2 \\ \qquad\qquad\quad | \\ C_{17}H_{35}COOCH \\ \qquad\qquad\quad | \\ C_{17}H_{35}COOCH_2 \end{array}$$

■ ***TIP*** The term 'fat' is used more generally in everyday speech, especially with regard to diet. Margarine is a dietary fat, but is not a fat in the sense meant here.

fatty acid: see *carboxylic acid*.

Fehling's solution: an alkaline solution of copper(II) tartrate.

- On heating with *aldehydes* it is reduced to a red or orange precipitate of copper(I) oxide.
- ***TIP*** Forming a *complex ion* from the copper(II) ion with a tartrate ion prevents its precipitation as copper(II) hydroxide when alkali is added. Fehling's solution has to be mixed immediately before use and contains quite concentrated sodium hydroxide. *Benedict's reagent* performs the same job and has neither disadvantage, and is now the preferred reagent.

fertiliser: a material intended to increase the fertility of soil.

- Most synthetic fertilisers contain ammonium nitrate or sulphate, or *urea*, as well as potassium and phosphate salts. So-called natural fertilisers include manure and compost.

fingerprint region: the region of the *infrared spectrum* of a substance between 910 and 1430 cm^{-1} (see *wave number*) where the pattern of the peaks is characteristic of that compound, even though the origins of all the peaks may not be known.

first electron affinity: the energy change per mole for the process

$$E(g) + e^- \longrightarrow E^-(g)$$

- ***TIP*** This is a case where the states are important.

first ionisation energy: the energy change per mole for the process

$$E(g) \longrightarrow E^+(g) + e^-$$

- ***TIP*** This is a case where the states are important.

flame test: a qualitative or quantitative test that uses the fact that some elements and their compounds give characteristic flame colours when heated in a blue Bunsen flame.

- ***e.g.*** In group 1 the principal colours are: lithium, red; sodium, orange/yellow; potassium, lilac; rubidium, red; caesium, blue. In group 2 the principal colours are: calcium, orange/red or brick red; strontium, red; barium, apple green. Others include copper, green with a blue centre.
- ***TIP*** The reds are impossible to tell apart by eye for Li, Rb and Sr, and other tests have to be used in addition to the flame test. However, the flame test is very useful for Na and K as there are no available precipitation reactions enabling their analysis.

fractional distillation: distillation that is designed to separate liquid mixtures according to their *boiling temperatures*.

- The mixture is heated in a flask bearing a fractionating column, the liquid of lowest boiling temperature coming off first. Liquid mixtures that form *azeotropes* cannot be completely separated by fractional distillation. The industrial process is rather different, being designed to work continuously and also to produce a range of mixtures with a particular boiling temperature range rather than pure

liquids with a single boiling temperature.

- ***e.g.*** Fractional distillation of petroleum produces fractions that are mixtures. Liquid air is fractionally distilled to produce oxygen and nitrogen.
- ***TIP*** Ethanol and water is one of the mixtures that cannot be separated by fractional distillation, because it produces an *azeotrope.*

free energy, ΔG (also called 'the Gibbs function' or 'the Gibbs free energy change')**:** it is defined by

$$\Delta G = \Delta H - T\Delta S$$

where ΔH is the *enthalpy change* and ΔS is the *entropy* change for a process at temperature T.

- For a *spontaneous chemical change,* ΔG is negative. It represents the maximum useful work that can be performed by a reacting system. For substances in their standard state, the corresponding standard free energy change is denoted ΔG^{o}.
- ***TIP*** It is the free energy that determines whether a reaction is feasible. Feasible reactions have $\Delta G < 0$. Equilibrium reactions settle at the composition that minimises the free energy of the system.

free radical: an atom or group of atoms having an unpaired electron.

- Radicals are reactive species — sometimes indiscriminately so.
- ***e.g.*** The first step in the chlorination of methane is the *homolytic fission* of chlorine molecules into two chlorine atoms under ultraviolet irradiation:

$$Cl_2 \longrightarrow 2Cl\bullet$$

The chlorine radical then attacks a methane molecule to give a methyl radical and hydrogen chloride:

$$Cl\bullet + CH_4 \longrightarrow \bullet CH_3 + HCl$$

- ***TIP*** Radical reactions often need ultraviolet light or employ a *radical* initiator such as oxygen or an organic *peroxide.*

freeze-drying: a technique of removing water from *aqueous solutions,* particularly ones that are sensitive to heat.

- The solution is frozen, and the pressure over the frozen solution reduced. Water sublimes from the solid, and is usually frozen out elsewhere at a very low temperature — that of solid carbon dioxide, –76°C, is common.
- ***TIP*** Freeze-dried instant coffee is a common product. Freeze-drying preserves some of the essential oils that give the coffee its flavour, which would be lost if the coffee solution were to be heated to remove the water.

freezing temperature (also called 'freezing point')**:** the temperature at which the *solid* and *liquid* phases of a substance are in equilibrium.

- The freezing temperature is depressed if a substance is impure, and this is the basis of the use of melting temperatures in assessing the purity of a substance.
- ***TIP*** The melting temperature and the freezing temperature are the same — which one you use just depends on whether you are melting a solid or cooling a liquid.

Friedel–Crafts reaction: the reaction of benzene or other *aromatic* compound with a halogen to give a *halogenoarene*, with a *halogenoalkane* to give an alkyl-substituted arene, or with an *acid chloride* to give an aromatic *ketone*.

Aluminium chloride is used as the *catalyst* in the reaction; with an acid chloride the catalyst is required in somewhat more than *stoichiometric* amount because it complexes with the product ketone.

e.g. In each case the reagents are heated under reflux in the presence of the catalyst:

$C_6H_6 + Cl_2 \longrightarrow C_6H_5Cl + HCl$
chlorobenzene

$C_6H_6 + CH_3Cl \longrightarrow C_6H_5CH_3 + HCl$
methylbenzene

$C_6H_6 + CH_3COCl \longrightarrow C_6H_5COCH_3 + HCl$
acetophenone

TIP Friedel–Crafts reactions do not always give the 'expected' product; thus use of 1-chloropropane, $CH_3CH_2CH_2Cl$, gives the attachment of the alkyl group on the 2-carbon with the product being $C_6H_5CH(CH_3)_2$. This is an example of a molecular rearrangement — not widely studied at this level.

fuel: a substance intended for burning to yield heat or light.

e.g. Wood, alkanes, coal.

TIP Many compounds that can burn are not used as fuels because they are too valuable as chemical precursors — the *alkenes* are a good example. Diamonds might be another, although they are difficult to light.

fullerenes: a family of carbon *allotropes* which give spherical (*buckminsterfullerene* C_{60}), ellipsoidal (C_{70} and others) and tubular structures. C_{60} consists of hexagons and pentagons; only 12 pentagons are required with the hexagons to make a spherical structure of whatever size. C_{60} is the smallest.

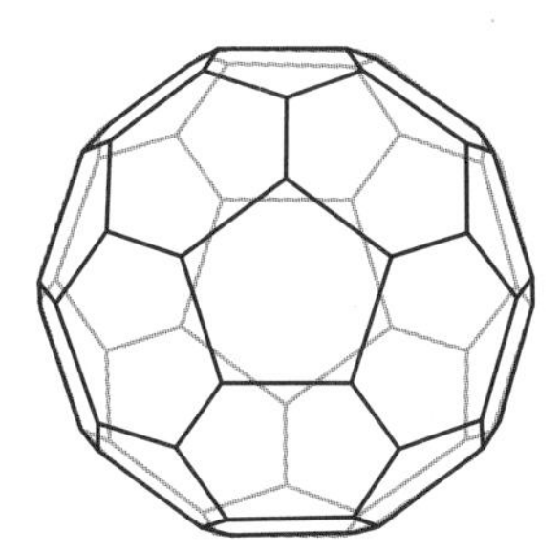

Buckminsterfullerene

functional group: an atom or group of atoms in an organic molecule that determines the characteristic chemical reactions of the molecule.

Such reactions are often (but not invariably) independent of the remainder of the molecule's structure, at least for relatively small molecules.

e.g. In every case the R– group can be *aryl* or *alkyl*:

Alkenes		**>C=C<**
Halogenoalkanes		R–**X** where X is a halogen
Alcohols:	primary	R–**CH_2OH**
	secondary	R–**CH(OH)**–R′
	tertiary	RR′R″**C–OH**
Aldehydes		R–**CHO**
Ketones		R–**CO**–R′
Carboxylic acids		R–**COOH**
Acid chlorides		R–**COCl**
Acid amides		R–**$CONH_2$**
Amines:	primary	R–**NH_2**
	secondary	R–**NH**–R′
	tertiary	R–**N**(R′)R″
Nitriles		R–**CN**

TIP Functional groups sometimes affect one another, sometimes they don't. Thus the three double bonds apparently present in *benzene* are delocalised and so do not behave like individual C=C bonds. In the carboxyl group, –COOH, the –OH part retains the ability to react with PCl_5, just as an alcohol would; but the carbonyl part >C=O does not react with *2,4-dinitrophenylhydrazine* in the way that aldehydes and ketones do.

gangue: the waste material remaining after an ore has been processed.

■ ***e.g.*** Bauxite is about 45% alumina with iron oxide and silica. The iron oxide and silica impurity left when the alumina has been extracted is the gangue.

gas: the state of matter characterised by neither volume nor shape being fixed for a fixed mass of the substance.

■ The molecules or atoms in the gas are free to move over large distances. Strictly speaking, a gas is at a temperature above that where the substance can be liquefied by exertion of pressure alone — the critical temperature. Below that temperature the gaseous state is more properly called a vapour.

■ ***TIP*** The distinction between a gas and a vapour is not usually important at A-level, but it is as well to know that it exists.

gas constant: in the equation of state for an ideal gas (that is, one not showing any intermolecular forces), the gas constant R is defined as

$$R = PV/T$$

for one mole of gas.

gel: a semi-solid phase that consists of a lattice of fibres in which water is absorbed.

■ ***e.g.*** Gelatin (jelly) is an elastic gel that is easily deformed. Silica gel, widely used as a drying agent because it absorbs water reversibly, is a rigid gel.

geometric isomerism: compounds of the form

a, c > C=C < b, d

have two isomers resulting from *restricted rotation* about the C=C bond. This in turn results from the sideways overlap of the *p-orbitals* constituting the pi-bond:

In addition, *a* and *c* must be different, as must *b* and *d*.

■ ***e.g.*** *Cis*- and *trans*-1,2-dichlorethene:

```
Cl        Cl        H         Cl
  \      /            \      /
   C == C              C == C
  /      \            /      \
 H        H         Cl        H
```

■ ***TIP*** Always draw these structures with the correct bond angles, around 120°; you will avoid a lot of confusion if you do. There are other ways of getting *cis–trans isomerism* in ring compounds and in transition element complexes that do not involve C=C bonds (*see restricted rotation*).

giant structure: an ionic, metallic or covalent structure where the bonding is of similar strength throughout the crystal.

■ ***e.g.*** Sodium chloride forms a giant ionic crystal, diamond a giant covalent one.

■ ***TIP*** Graphite is often regarded as a giant structure; in fact it is a stack of giant covalent layers, rather like a pile of paper.

Gibbs free energy or Gibbs function, ΔG: this is the maximum work, other than work of expansion, that can be obtained from a chemical system. It is defined by

$$\Delta G = \Delta H - T\Delta S$$

where ΔH is the enthalpy and ΔS the entropy change for the process at temperature T.

■ ***TIP*** ΔG is negative for all spontaneous processes. Equilibrium reactions settle at a composition that makes ΔG a minimum.

glass: a hard material that does not have a crystalline structure and is regarded as a supercooled liquid (see *supercooling*).

■ ***e.g.*** Ordinary soft glass is a mixture of calcium and sodium silicates; hard glass (e.g. Pyrex) has borax added and is often called borosilicate glass. It has a much higher softening temperature than soft glass.

glass electrode: the ion-sensitive electrode found in the pH meter, whose potential depends on the concentration of the hydrogen ions in which it is dipped.

■ It is made from a high-conductivity lithium glass.

■ ***TIP*** The electrode is very thin and breaks easily.

graphite: the most stable (thermodynamically) allotrope of carbon, consisting of planes of flat hexagons with delocalised electrons and weak van der Waals bonds between the layers.

■ ***TIP*** There are two forms of graphite depending on how three adjacent layers stack. The electrical conductivity of graphite is parallel to the layers only, unlike metals, where conduction is equal in all directions.

gravimetric analysis: quantitative analysis based on weighing a precipitate.

■ ***e.g.*** Sulphates can be determined by the addition of excess barium chloride solution, followed by filtration, washing and drying of the precipitate, which is then weighed. Gravimetric analysis requires very careful technique.

Grignard reagent: an organic compound formed by reaction of a *halogenoalkane* or *halogenoarene* with magnesium metal in a *solvent* of dry ether.

- Grignard reagents can be used to make *alcohols* or *carboxylic acids*.
- ***e.g.*** $C_2H_5Br + Mg \longrightarrow C_2H_5MgBr$
- ***TIP*** The reagents and the apparatus must be completely dry. A *catalyst* of iodine is sometimes needed. The Grignard reagent is not isolated and is used in the solution in which it was made. The reaction is tricky; solutions of common Grignard reagents are commercially available and are a sensible idea. François August Victor Grignard won the Nobel prize for his work in 1912; not without controversy, as some suggested later that he had filched his ideas from his supervisor. Envy or truth? Who knows.

group: a vertical division of the *periodic table*.

- The main group elements, variously called groups IA, IIA, IIIB–VIIB and 0, or 1–7 and 0, or 1, 2, 13–18, depending on the source and the age of the book, have elements with the same outer electron shell structure in a given group.
- ***TIP*** There is no particular reason why the periodic table should be arranged this way. Mendeleyev's original table had the groups horizontally; there have been spiral versions of the table, even three-dimensional ones. It is not always clear what points are being made by these latter versions. It is interesting to speculate on who might have had the temerity to change Mendeleyev's original. *Transition elements* are also arranged in groups, but the vertical similarities are not very great and the outer-shell electronic structures often differ.

group 1 (formerly 'group IA')**:** the alkali metals lithium, sodium, potassium, rubidium, caesium, francium.

- ***TIP*** Don't quote any reactions of francium in order to be different — no one has ever seen any, and it is an all-too-popular choice anyway. Don't use an alkali metal/water (or even worse, alkali metal/acid) reaction as a source of hydrogen — it is a once-only experiment!

group 2 (formerly 'group IIA')**:** the alkaline earth metals beryllium, magnesium, calcium, strontium, barium, radium.

- ***TIP*** Don't use radium in any general example for group 2.

group 7 (formerly 'group VIIB', most recently called 'group 17')**:** the halogens ('salt-formers') fluorine, chlorine, bromine, iodine, astatine.

- ***TIP*** Don't use fluorine or astatine as general examples of group 7 chemistry: many of fluorine's reactions are unusual compared with the rest of the group and no large amount of astatine has ever been seen, although its chemistry is quite well understood.

Haber process: the reaction of hydrogen and nitrogen in the presence of an iron/aluminium oxide/potassium oxide *catalyst* at around 350°C and 350 atm pressure to give ammonia.

■ ***TIP*** The exact conditions employed depend on the extent of the market. In the USA, a larger market justifies the expense of higher pressures up to 1000 atm, which give higher yields. The problems of containment of high pressure have been solved, so this is not something that makes the Haber process difficult. The principal costs in high-pressure processes are:

- the capital cost of the pressure vessel (one-off),
- the ongoing costs of maintenance and, by far the most important,
- the cost of fuel to drive the compressors.

half-equation: an equation involving electrons that shows the *oxidation* or *reduction* of a given species without specifying the identity of the oxidising or reducing agent.

■ Two half-equations added in such a way as to make the number of electrons transferred the same (because they are the same electrons) produce a full *redox reaction* equation.

■ ***e.g.*** The half-equation for the reduction of potassium manganate(VII) in acidic solution is

$$MnO_4^-(aq) + 8H^+(aq) + 5e^- \longrightarrow Mn^{2+}(aq) + 4H_2O(l)$$

which applies whatever the chosen reducing agent. If this be iron(II), say, the half-equation for the oxidation is

$$Fe^{2+}(aq) \longrightarrow Fe^{3+}(aq) + e^-$$

The combination of the two is

$$MnO_4^-(aq) + 5Fe^{2+}(aq) + 8H^+(aq) \longrightarrow Mn^{2+}(aq) + 5Fe^{3+}(aq) + 4H_2O(l)$$

half-life: the time taken for the number of radioactive nuclei present at some arbitrary initial time t to decay; or the time taken for the concentration of a reagent to halve during a chemical reaction.

■ ***TIP*** The half-life for radioactive decay and for first order chemical reactions depends only on the nuclide or the reaction and not on the original amount

of substance present. The half-life is not constant for other than first-order reactions.

halide: compound of the *halogens*, group 7.

halide ions, test for: the test *solution* is made acidic with nitric acid (test with blue litmus) and silver nitrate solution is added; any precipitate that forms is treated with ammonia solution.

e.g.

Ion	Precipitate	With ammonia
Chloride	White	Soluble dilute
Bromide	Cream	Insoluble dilute, soluble concentrated
Iodide	Yellow	Insoluble, though may become paler

TIP Concentrated solutions of sulphates will precipitate silver sulphate in this test; it has a pearly appearance quite unlike the dense white of silver chloride.

Hall–Héroult cell: the cell having a graphite *anode* and *cathode* that is used to electrolyse a molten mixture of cryolite, Na_3AlF_6 (90%), aluminium oxide, Al_2O_3 (5%) and calcium fluoride, CaF_2 (5%) to produce aluminium.

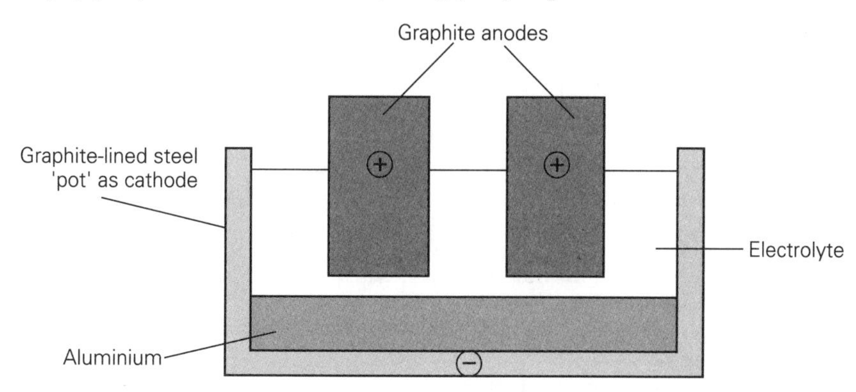

TIP Hall and Héroult discovered the method independently and then made quite a number of lawyers rich by arguing over precedence. They eventually agreed on the nature of each other's contribution. The cathode is actually mostly the layer of molten aluminium on the bottom of the cell.

haloform reaction: the reaction between a methyl *ketone*, CH_3CO–, or a methyl *secondary alcohol*, $CH_3CH(OH)$–, and a halogen in sodium hydroxide solution to give CHX_3, where X is a halogen atom.

It is mostly used analytically to show the presence of the groups stated using iodine and sodium hydroxide solution: a yellow precipitate of iodoform, CHI_3, forms. When the halogen is iodine it is called the *iodoform reaction*. It is also used commercially to make chloroform, $CHCl_3$, from propanone and bleaching powder, calcium hypochlorite.

e.g. $CH_3COCH_3 + 3I_2 + 4NaOH \longrightarrow CHI_3 + CH_3COONa + 3NaI + 3H_2O$

TIP The haloform reaction is not a general test for ketones or for secondary alcohols.

halogen: one of the elements of group 7: fluorine, chlorine, bromine, iodine and astatine.

TIP Do not use either fluorine or astatine as an exemplar halogen if you have a choice. Fluorine has some atypical properties, and although the chemistry of astatine is quite well understood, no one has ever had enough of it to see.

halogenating agent: a substance used to introduce a halogen atom into an organic compound.

e.g. Halogens themselves can be used:

$$CH_4 + Cl_2 \longrightarrow CH_3Cl + HCl$$

Phosphorus(V) chloride is commonly used to halogenate alcohols or acids:

$$2CH_3CH_2OH + PCl_5 \longrightarrow 2CH_3CH_2Cl + POCl_3 + 2HCl$$
$$2CH_3COOH + PCl_5 \longrightarrow 2CH_3COCl + POCl_3 + 2HCl$$

halogenoalkane: compound of the form R–X, where R is an alkyl group and X is a halogen atom.

e.g. Iodoethane, CH_3CH_2I.

halogenoarene: an *aromatic compound* having a halogen atom attached directly to the benzene ring.

e.g. Chlorobenzene, C_6H_5Cl.

hard water: water that contains calcium or magnesium ions, and which will not lather very well with *soap*, forming a scum instead.

Temporary hardness, which is due to calcium or magnesium hydrogen carbonate, can be removed by boiling; permanent hardness, which is due to calcium or magnesium sulphate, cannot. Hardness can be removed by *ion exchange*.

hazards: possible risks that need to be assessed for each experiment.

To assess hazards you need information about such things as flammability, toxicity and scale of the experiment, as well as the expertise of the experimenter. There are very few reactions that cannot be done given suitable conditions, but these need careful evaluation. (See also *risk assessment*.)

TIP Do not quote global requirements such as lab coat and goggles — those are understood. You should consider the hazards peculiar to the experiment concerned.

heat of...: see *enthalpy of...*

Henderson equation: the equation, derived from the expression for K_a, that enables the calculation of the pH of a buffer.

For a mixture of a *weak acid*, HA, and its salt, NaA:

$$K_a = \frac{[H^+][A^-]}{[HA]}$$

thus

$$[H^+] = \frac{K_a[HA]}{[A^-]}$$

Taking the negative logarithm of both sides:

$$-\log[H^+] = -\log K_a - \log \frac{[HA]}{[A^-]}$$

or

$$pH = pK_a + \log \frac{[A^-]}{[HA]}$$

which is the Henderson equation.

Knowing the concentration of HA and of A^- enables the calculation of the pH. The dissociation of HA is so small that its concentration in the mixture is nearly its initial concentration, and virtually all the anions, A^-, come from the salt, so their concentration is its concentration.

- ***e.g.*** The pH of a solution 0.1 mol dm^{-3} in sodium ethanoate and 0.05 mol dm^{-3} in ethanoic acid, whose K_a value is 1.8×10^{-5} mol dm^{-3}, is

  $pH = 4.74 + \log(0.10/0.050) = 4.74 + 0.3 = 5.04$

herbicide: a substance designed to kill plants.

- It may be non-selective, such as potassium chlorate, $KClO_3$, which kills all plants; or it may be selective, like 2,4-dichlorophenoxyacetic acid (2,4-D), which kills dicotyledons but not monocotyledons (grasses).

Hess's law (of constant heat summation): the *enthalpy change* (heat change at constant pressure) for a reaction A ⟶ B is the same whether the reaction proceeds in one or in several steps, e.g. A ⟶ C ⟶ D ⟶ B.

- ***e.g.*** All calculations involving ΔH_f, ΔH_c, the *Born–Haber cycle* and *mean bond energies* are based on Hess's law.
- ***TIP*** Hess's law is a subset of the law of conservation of energy, and applies to heat changes. Do not refer to energy changes.

heterogeneous equilibrium: an *equilibrium* where the substances are not all in the same phase.

- Solid phases are not included in the expression for the equilibrium constant.
- ***e.g.*** The thermal dissociation of calcium carbonate in a closed system is a heterogeneous equilibrium:

  $CaCO_3(s) \rightleftharpoons CaO(s) + CO_2(g)$

  $K_p = p(CO_2)$

- ***TIP*** Ask your teacher why the solid phase is omitted in K_p.

heterolytic fission: the breaking of a *covalent bond* so that the electron pair remains with one of the fragments and therefore gives it a negative charge; the other fragment is positive.

- ***e.g.*** The use of aluminium chloride in the *Friedel–Crafts reaction* effectively causes heterolytic fission of the chlorine molecule:

  $Cl_2 \longrightarrow Cl^- + Cl^+$

hexaqua ion: a metal ion that bonds to six molecules of water.

■ The oxygen atom in the water donates a pair of electrons to vacant orbitals on the metal ion.

■ ***e.g.*** There are lots of examples, including: $[Cu(H_2O)_6]^{2+}$; $[Fe(H_2O)_6]^{2+}$; $[Cr(H_2O)_6]^{3+}$; $[Al(H_2O)_6]^{3+}$.

Hofmann reaction: the reaction between an acid amide, $RCONH_2$, and bromine, followed by sodium hydroxide solution, giving an amine with one fewer carbon atoms than the amide.

■ Essentially the reaction removes the carbonyl group.

■ ***e.g.*** $RCONH_2 + Br_2 + 4NaOH \longrightarrow RNH_2 + 2NaBr + Na_2CO_3 + 2H_2O$

■ ***TIP*** Always make clear that the reaction is with bromine followed by sodium hydroxide solution — it is a two-stage reaction.

homogeneous equilibrium: an *equilibrium* reaction where all the substances involved are in the same phase.

■ ***e.g.*** Liquid phase: $CH_3CH_2OH + CH_3COOH \rightleftharpoons CH_3COOCH_2CH_3 + H_2O$.
Gas phase: $PCl_5(g) \rightleftharpoons PCl_3(g) + Cl_2(g)$.

homologous series: a series of organic compounds in which:

- each member has the same general formula
- each member differs from the immediately preceding and succeeding ones by CH_2
- the series shows a trend in physical properties, such as *melting* and *boiling temperature* and viscosity
- all members have similar chemical properties (though the first member of a given series may have some peculiarities)

■ ***e.g.*** The alkanes:

- have the general formula C_nH_{2n+2}
- differ by CH_2: CH_4, C_2H_6, C_3H_8,...
- show a gradual increase in melting and boiling temperature and viscosity as the carbon chain length increases
- burn similarly to give CO_2 and water, and react with chlorine in the presence of ultraviolet light

homolytic fission: the splitting of a *covalent bond* so that one electron is retained by each fragment, which is therefore a *radical.*

■ ***e.g.*** The first step in the photohalogenation of alkanes is the homolytic splitting of chlorine molecules:

$$Cl_2 \longrightarrow 2Cl\bullet$$

hydrated ion: on dissolving in water, ions attract the *polar molecules* of water and become hydrated with a variable number of water molecules.

■ The bonds are electrostatic rather than covalent as in the case of hexaqua ions. The smaller the ion and the higher its charge, i.e. the higher its *charge density,* the more hydration there will be and the higher the *enthalpy of hydration,* ΔH_{hyd}.

hydride: a compound of hydrogen and one other element.

There are four varieties:

- ionic, containing the H^- ion; these form only with electropositive metals such as those in groups 1 and 2
- complex, such as $LiAlH_4$, which has H^- complexed with AlH_3 to give the AlH_4^- ion
- covalent — formed by most non-metals; examples include ammonia, water, hydrocarbons
- interstitial — hydrogen atoms are inserted into gaps in the crystal lattices of *transition elements*; these hydrides do not have a fixed composition, so are called non-stoichiometric compounds

hydrogenation: the addition of hydrogen across a multiple bond.

e.g. The hydrogenation of ethene to give ethane:

$$H_2C{=}CH_2 + H_2 \longrightarrow CH_3CH_3$$

hydrogen bond: an electrostatic bond formed between hydrogen attached to nitrogen, oxygen or fluorine and a nitrogen, oxygen or fluorine atom on another molecule.

The hydrogen therefore bridges the two electronegative atoms, which need not be the same. The bond is linear; in H–F···H– it has a strength of about 150 kJ mol^{-1}, but usually its strength is between 20 and 60 kJ mol^{-1}. Hydrogen bonding is sometimes important in *solubility* considerations — thus sugars are very water-soluble because their numerous –OH groups can hydrogen bond with the water *solvent*.

e.g. Hydrogen bonding is found between the molecules of HF, H_2O and NH_3, and gives these hydrides unusually high boiling temperatures when compared with the other hydrides in their respective groups. The long hydrogen bonds in ice hold the water molecules further apart than in the liquid, and therefore reduce the density of the solid compared with that of the liquid. Hydrogen bonds hold the two halves of the DNA helix together, and are responsible for much of the bonding leading to the structural features of proteins.

hydrogen electrode, standard: the reference electrode for all electrochemical measurements.

It consists of a platinum foil coated in platinum black (finely divided platinum) dipping into a solution of hydrochloric acid with $[H^+]$ = 1 mol dm^{-3}. Hydrogen gas is bubbled over the surface of the platinum at a pressure of 1 atm. The electrode behaves exactly as an electrode made of (non-conducting) hydrogen would, and allows the equilibrium:

$$2H^+(aq) + 2e^- \rightleftharpoons H_2(g)$$

to be set up. The electrode has a defined reduction potential at 298 K of 0.00 V.

hydrolysis: a reaction that decomposes a molecule by means of water, perhaps requiring acid or base catalysis.

e.g. Hydrolysis of *acyl chlorides* does not require a catalyst; the reaction is violent with water alone:

$$CH_3COCl + H_2O \longrightarrow CH_3COOH + HCl$$

Hydrolysis of *esters* can use acid catalysis (dilute sulphuric acid) when an *equilibrium* mixture is formed:

$$CH_3COOCH_2CH_3 + H_2O \rightleftharpoons CH_3COOH + CH_3CH_2OH$$

With sodium hydroxide the ester is hydrolysed in a non-equilibrium reaction:

$$CH_3COOCH_2CH_3 + NaOH \longrightarrow CH_3COONa + CH_3CH_2OH$$

hydrophilic: literally 'water loving', it describes the parts of molecules that seek out an aqueous environment, including –OH and –COOH groups.

e.g. The soap sodium stearate, $C_{17}H_{35}COOH$, has a hydrophilic –COOH group, which is responsible for the ability of the soap to act as an *emulsifying agent.*

hydrophobic: the parts of a molecule that seek out non-aqueous environments.

e.g. The soap sodium stearate, $C_{17}H_{35}COOH$, has a hydrophobic $C_{17}H_{35}$– group, which is responsible for the ability of the soap to act as an *emulsifying agent.* The hydrophobic group dissolves in the grease droplets leaving the *hydrophilic* carboxyl group on the surface of the droplet.

hydroxide: compound containing the OH^- ion, which is therefore predominantly ionic.

Hydroxides are generally basic or amphoteric.

e.g. Copper(II) hydroxide, $Cu(OH)_2$, is basic; aluminium hydroxide $Al(OH)_3$ is amphoteric.

hydroxonium ion, H_3O^+: the ion found in all *Brønsted–Lowry acids.*

hydroxyl group: the –OH group covalently bonded in a molecular structure.

e.g. Alcohols and carboxylic acids contain it, as do pure sulphuric and nitric acids, amongst many other examples.

ice: the solid form of water.

- At room pressure ice consists of six water molecules joined by hydrogen bonding into chair-shaped rings. Layers of these rings give a structure reminiscent of diamond. The hydrogen bonds push the molecules further apart than they are in the liquid, so ice has a lower density than liquid water and floats in it. The resultant convection currents in an iced drink save you the bother of having to stir it.
- **TIP** At higher pressures there are different solid modifications of ice — nine, in fact. Kurt Vonnegut used ice-IX in his story ***Cat's Cradle*** as being a solid form at 100°C. It is — but the pressure has to be several tens of thousands of atmospheres.

ideal gas: a gas that has no intermolecular or interatomic forces, and which is described by the ideal gas equation $PV = nRT$.

- **TIP** Real gases do have such forces; they could not be liquefied otherwise.

indicator: a substance whose colour in solution depends either on the pH (acid–base indicators) or on the presence or otherwise of *oxidising agents* (redox indicators).

- Acid–base indicators are *weak acids* themselves; if we represent the molecule as HIn, the dissociation

$$HIn \rightleftharpoons H^+ + In^-$$

depends on the pH of the solution to which the indicator is added. In the case of phenolphthalein, HIn is colourless and In^- is magenta; for methyl orange, HIn is red and In^- is yellow. Not all indicators change colour at the same pH; phenolphthalein changes at pH 8.3–10.0, methyl orange at pH 3.1–4.4. (See also *titration curve*.)

induced dipole force: a force induced in one molecule by the approach of another molecule which has a dipole, whether permanent or temporary.

- This results in an induced dipole–dipole or induced dipole–induced dipole attractive force, known usually (but not always accurately) as a *van der Waals force*.

inductive effect: the drawing of charge towards, or release of charge from, substituent groups or atoms within an organic molecule, which results in a dipole in the molecule.

■ ***e.g.*** Chloroethanoic acid, $ClCH_2COOH$, is a stronger acid than ethanoic acid, CH_3COOH. This is attributed in part to the electron-withdrawing effect of the chlorine atom, which polarises the O–H bond more compared with the same bond in ethanoic acid itself.

industrial methylated spirit (IMS): a mixture of about 90% ethanol, 5% methanol and 5% water.

■ It is a colourless liquid, and is poisonous. The methanol is added to make the spirit unfit to drink. It is usable for most processes that require ethanol.

■ ***TIP*** The distillation of IMS to remove the methanol is both difficult and illegal.

inert gas: see *noble gas*.

inert pair effect: this is a name, not an explanation, for the feature found in the elements of groups 3, 4 and 5 where the penultimate element is most stable in the higher oxidation state for the group, whereas the last element is more stable in the lower state.

■ Thus in group 3, In(+3) rather than In(+1), but Tl(+1) rather than Tl(+3); in group 4, Sn(+4) but Pb(+2); in group 5, Sb(+5) but Bi(+3). The example in group 4 is the most important and leads to the oxidising properties of PbO_2.

■ ***TIP*** Knowing something is not the same as knowing the name of something.

infrared (IR): The region of the electromagnetic spectrum between about 10^{-3} and 10^{-6} m.

infrared spectrum: the trace produced when infrared light is passed through a film or paste of an organic compound, arising from stretching or bending vibrations of the molecule.

■ If a bond is polar it will absorb certain frequencies of the light and this shows as peaks in the spectrum. Certain groups are characteristic and aid the identification of a compound; the region between 910 and 1430 cm^{-1} is generally characteristic of a given compound and is called the *fingerprint region*. The absorbances in this region come from bending vibrations of the molecule, and even fairly simple molecules have many such modes of vibration. Traditionally the zero of infrared absorbance is along the top of the spectrum, the peaks actually being troughs. A molecular vibration gives rise to an infrared absorption only if it results in a change in the molecular dipole moment (see *polar molecule, permanent dipole*).

■ ***e.g.*** The infrared spectra of ethanol and of propanone are shown below. Ethanol shows a broad peak around 3500 cm^{-1}, characteristic of hydrogen bonded –OH groups; propanone has a peak around 1700 cm^{-1}, characteristic of a ketone C=O group.

IR spectrum of ethanol:

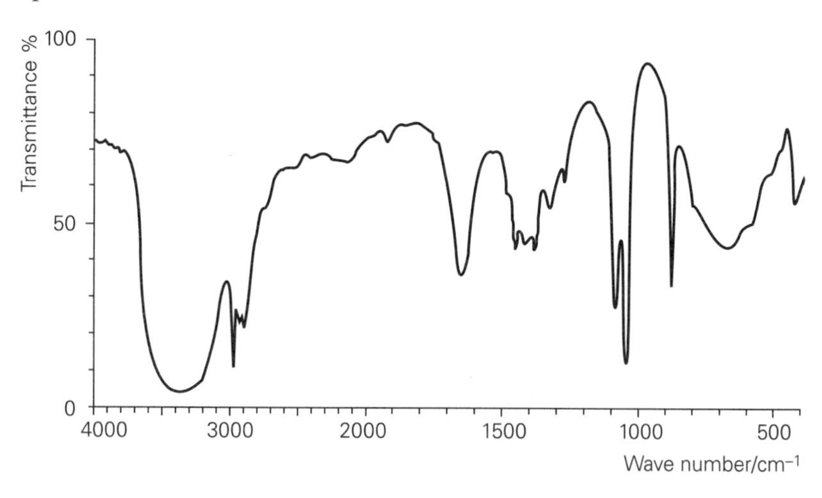

IR spectrum of propanone:

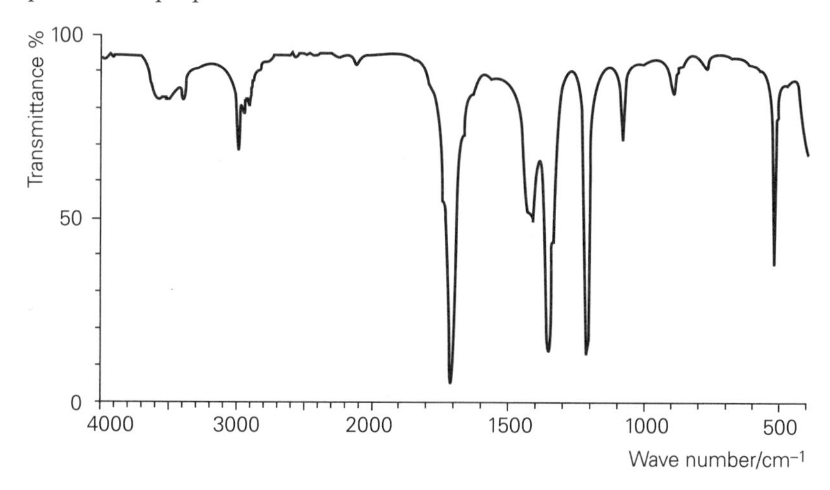

intermolecular forces: the forces between molecules, as distinct from those within molecules.

- These may be attractive or repulsive, but usually the term refers to attractions. The strongest of these forces is the *hydrogen bond,* followed by permanent dipole–permanent dipole, permanent dipole–induced dipole, and then induced dipole–induced dipole. These are often generically called *van der Waals forces.*
- ***TIP*** The phrase 'forces holding molecules together' is ambiguous and should be avoided. Make clear whether intermolecular forces or *intramolecular forces* are being considered.

interstitial compound: a compound whose structure results from small atoms being absorbed into the spaces in a crystal lattice.

- ***e.g.*** Many *transition element* hydrides are interstitial; hydrogen is absorbed between the atoms of the metal. Such hydrides do not usually have a fixed composition, i.e. they are non-stoichiometric compounds.

intramolecular forces: forces bonding within molecules, as distinct from those between molecules.

■ Covalent bonds are intramolecular forces, though hydrogen bonding can occur intramolecularly as well.

■ ***TIP*** The phrase 'forces holding molecules together' is ambiguous and should be avoided. Make clear whether *intermolecular forces* or intramolecular forces are being considered.

iodoform reaction: the reaction between a solution of iodine in sodium hydroxide and compounds containing CH_3CO– or $CH_3CH(OH)$– groups.

■ A yellow precipitate of the antiseptic-smelling iodoform, tri-iodomethane, CHI_3, is obtained. It is usually used as a test for methyl *ketones* or methyl *secondary alcohols* in qualitative analysis.

■ ***e.g.*** $CH_3COCH_3 + 4NaOH + 3I_2 \longrightarrow CHI_3 + CH_3COONa + 3NaI + 3H_2O$

■ ***TIP*** The reaction is not a general test for ketones or for secondary alcohols. A similar reaction using chlorine and sodium hydroxide together with propanone can be used to make chloroform, $CHCl_3$.

ion: an atom or group of atoms bearing a charge because of having more or fewer electrons than protons.

ion exchange: a process where ions held on the surface of a solid are exchanged for other ions present in solution.

■ ***e.g.*** Ion exchange resins are widely used in water softeners to treat *hard water*. They consist of a modified polystyrene material that has sodium ions on the surface. These exchange with the calcium ions in the water, so that the exit water contains sodium salts rather than calcium salts, and is therefore soft. Deionised water comes from a mixed resin that exchanges cations for H^+ and anions for OH^-, which then give water. Deionised water has not had non-ionic impurities removed, so it is not as pure as distilled water.

ionic bonding: the attraction between ions of opposite charge giving rise to *giant structures* of ionic crystal *lattices*.

■ ***e.g.*** Sodium chloride, aluminium oxide, calcium nitrate.

■ ***TIP*** Strictly, there is no such thing as an ionic bond; the electrostatic attractions in the crystal are not localised, but spread throughout the whole lattice.

ionic equation: an equation where the ions that do not enter into a reaction — the 'spectator ions' — are omitted.

■ The use of ionic equations leads to greater simplicity and therefore clarity.

■ ***e.g.*** The reaction between chlorine and cold sodium hydroxide solution is not greatly different whether written as a 'full' or as an ionic equation:

$$Cl_2(g) + 2OH^-(aq) \longrightarrow Cl^-(aq) + OCl^-(aq) + 2H_2O(l)$$

$$Cl_2(g) + 2NaOH(aq) \longrightarrow NaCl(aq) + NaOCl(aq) + 2H_2O(l)$$

That for the reaction of potassium manganate(VII) with iron(II) sulphate is a different matter:

$2KMnO_4(aq) + 10FeSO_4(aq) + 8H_2SO_4(aq)$
$\longrightarrow 2MnSO_4(aq) + 5Fe_2(SO_4)_3(aq) + 8H_2O(l) + K_2SO_4(aq)$

$MnO_4^-(aq) + 5Fe^{2+}(aq) + 8H^+(aq) \longrightarrow Mn^{2+}(aq) + 5Fe^{3+}(aq) + 4H_2O(l)$

ionic model of crystal lattice: the *lattice energy* of an ionic crystal can be calculated using three-dimensional geometry together with Coulomb's law, which describes the force between ions in terms of their charges and distance apart.

- In this case the ions are assumed not to share any electron density — the charges are completely separated.
- ***e.g.*** The experimental ΔH_{latt} for caesium fluoride, CsF (from the *Born–Haber cycle*), is –716 kJ mol^{-1}, the calculated value being –728 kJ mol^{-1}. The difference is small and shows that CsF is essentially ionic.
- ***TIP*** The difference between the calculated lattice energy and the experimentally obtained value is a measure of the deviation of a crystal from wholly ionic character.

ionic product for water, *K*$_w$: a fixed value derived from the product of the concentrations of hydroxide and hydrogen ions in water at 25°C:

$[H^+][OH^-] = 1 \times 10^{-14}$ mol^2 dm^{-6}

(See also K_w.)

ionic radius: the effective radius of an ion in a crystal *lattice*, as determined by *X-ray crystallography.*

ionisation energy: the energy change per mole for the removal in the gas phase of an electron from an atom, ion or molecule.

- ***e.g.*** In each case the ionisation energy is the energy change per mole for the following processes:

from an atom:

$Na(g) \longrightarrow Na^+(g) + e^-$ (first ionisation energy of sodium)

from an ion:

$Na^+(g) \longrightarrow Na^{2+}(g) + e^-$ (second ionisation energy of sodium)

from a molecule:

$O_2(g) \longrightarrow O_2^+(g) + e^-$

ion-selective electrode: an electrode whose potential is sensitive to a particular ion.

- ***e.g.*** The glass electrode used in the pH meter is the commonest example, and is sensitive to the concentration of hydrogen ions. Water pollution ecologists use an electrode that is sensitive to dissolved oxygen to test river water.

isomerism: the ability of molecules of a given molecular formula to possess different structural formulae.

- ***e.g.*** Examples can be found under *geometric isomerism, structural isomerism and optical isomerism.*

isothermal process: a process that occurs at constant temperature.

isotope: isotopes are atoms that have the same *atomic number* (so are atoms of the same element) but different *mass number*, owing to differing numbers of neutrons in the nucleus.

TIP All elements have isotopes; the term is not synonymous with radioactivity. The electron structures for isotopes of a given atom are all the same, and, therefore, so is their chemistry. Do not refer to 'varying' numbers of neutrons.

IUPAC: the International Union of Pure and Applied Chemistry, which monitors and maintains international standards of, amongst other things, nomenclature in chemistry.

K_a: the acid dissociation constant. For the dissociation

$$HA(aq) \rightleftharpoons H^+(aq) + A^-(aq)$$

$$K_a = \frac{[H^+][A^-]}{[HA]}$$

It has units of mol dm^{-3}.

- *e.g.* K_a for ethanoic acid CH_3COOH at 25°C is 1.8×10^{-5} mol dm^{-3}; most organic acids have lower values than this and are *weak acids*. *Strong acids* have large values of K_a.

K_c: the equilibrium constant for a reaction in terms of the equilibrium *concentrations* at a stated temperature.

- The concentrations are shown by the notation [X], meaning 'the concentration of X'.
- *e.g.* $CH_3CH_2OH + CH_3COOH \rightleftharpoons CH_3COOCH_2CH_3 + H_2O$

$$K_c = \frac{[CH_3COOCH_2CH_3]\ [H_2O]}{[CH_3CH_2OH][CH_3COOH]}$$

- ***TIP*** Don't forget that the equation used to represent the reaction must be quoted together with the expression for K_c. Do not use square brackets to mean anything else — in particular do not use them in expressions for K_p.

Kekulé structure of benzene: the cyclic structure of benzene showing alternate double and single bonds.

- Friedrich Kekulé von Stradonitz suggested the structure in 1865, but also knew that it could not be the whole story. Such an apparent *alkene* would react immediately with bromine, but the fact that it does not was known at the time. The Kekulé structure (below left) is a perfectly acceptable way of representing benzene in equations and structures as everyone knows what it means. An alternative representation is shown on the right.

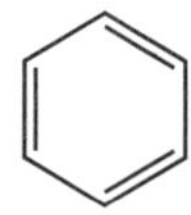 

Kelvin scale: the absolute or thermodynamic scale of temperature.

■ 0 K (no ° sign) is absolute zero, the lowest possible temperature. The freezing temperature of water is 273.2 K.

ketone: a compound of the form RCOR′, containing the carbonyl group >C=O.

■ ***e.g.*** The simplest ketone is propanone (acetone), CH_3COCH_3.

kinetics: the quantitative study of the dependence of reaction rate on variables such as concentration, pressure and temperature.

■ Information can thereby be obtained on *reaction mechanisms.*

■ ***e.g.*** The reaction between 2-bromo-2-methylpropane and hydroxide ions in aqueous ethanol shows that the rate is proportional only to the concentration of the organic compound, that is:

rate = k[2-bromo-2-methylpropane]

This means that the hydroxide ion is not part of the *rate-determining step*, so the mechanism for the reaction must have at least two steps. The reaction is an example of an S_N1 reaction.

kinetic stability: if two substances react very slowly because the *activation energy* for the reaction is high, the reaction system shows kinetic stability.

■ ***e.g.*** Most organic compounds are able to burn fairly easily, but do not do so unless ignited. The activation energy barrier for the combustion is too high for spontaneous ignition at room temperature.

■ ***TIP*** You may only talk about kinetic stability in terms of a reaction, not in terms of a single substance.

knocking (also called 'pre-ignition' or 'pinking')**:** the premature ignition of the *fuel*/air mixture in an internal combustion engine, before the spark has fired.

■ As pre-ignition occurs on the upstroke of the piston, knocking reduces power output and can cause serious physical damage to the engine.

K_p: the equilibrium constant for an equilibrium in the gas phase in terms of *partial pressures*, at a specified temperature.

■ ***e.g.*** For the dissociation of phosphorus(v) chloride in the gas phase:

$$PCl_5(g) \rightleftharpoons PCl_3(g) + Cl_2(g)$$

$$K_p = \frac{p(PCl_3)\ p(Cl_2)}{p(PCl_5)}$$

■ ***TIP*** Do not forget that the equation used to represent the reaction must be quoted together with the expression for K_p. Do not use square brackets in expressions for K_p.

K_w: the ionic product for water:

$$K_w = [H^+][OH^-] = 1 \times 10^{-14}\ mol^2\ dm^{-6} \text{ at } 25°C$$

■ This value is constant in all aqueous solutions at 25°C, so the concentration of H^+ or OH^- can be found if the other is known.

■ ***TIP*** This shows that in the most alkaline of solutions there are still H^+ ions, and in the most acidic solutions there are still OH^- ions. A neutral solution is

one where $[H^+] = [OH^-]$, which is at pH 7 only at 25°C. The value of K_w is different at other temperatures and so, therefore, is the pH of a neutral solution. At 0°C it is about pH 8, at 100°C about pH 6.

lattice: the three-dimensional array of atoms, ions or molecules in a crystal.

lattice energy, ΔH_{latt}: the energy change for the process where gaseous ions (infinitely far apart, and therefore not already interacting) combine to give a mole of solid ionic compound — it is therefore exothermic.

- Some sources define ΔH_{latt} the other way; that is, as the energy change for formation of the infinitely separated gaseous ions from one mole of ionic compound, and therefore endothermic.
- ***e.g.*** The lattice energy of sodium chloride is the energy change for

  $Na^+(g) + Cl^-(g) \longrightarrow NaCl(s)$

lattice enthalpy: often used as equivalent in meaning to lattice energy, but it is the heat change for the process above. The difference between the two values is generally small.

layer lattice: a *lattice* in which there are more or less well-defined layers, where the bonds within the layers are stronger than the bonds between the layers.

- ***e.g.*** By far the best-known example is *graphite*, where the bonds within layers are covalent but the bonds between the layers are *van der Waals forces*. The layers can therefore slide over one another and graphite feels greasy.

lead–acid battery: an *electrochemical cell* in which the positive pole consists of a porous plate of lead(IV) oxide and the negative pole consists of lead. The *electrolyte* is sulphuric acid.

- The reactions on discharge are:

  $PbO_2 + 4H^+ + SO_4^{2-} + 2e^- \longrightarrow PbSO_4 + 2H_2O$

  $Pb + SO_4^{2-} \longrightarrow PbSO_4 + 2e^-$

  These reactions can be reversed by passing current into the cell, so charging it. The cell can deliver extremely heavy currents, up to 400 amps for a short time; this is why they are used in cars, which demand such currents on starting.
- ***TIP*** The disadvantage of the lead–acid battery as a primary source of power is its weight. This is why milk floats are slow vehicles.

Le Chatelier's principle: a qualitative statement used to predict what happens

when the conditions under which an equilibrium exists are changed.

■ The statement is: 'If the conditions under which an equilibrium exists are changed, the position of equilibrium alters in such a way as to tend to oppose the change in conditions'. Thus:

- if the reactant concentration is increased, the equilibrium 'moves to the right' (that is, more product is formed)
- if products are removed, the equilibrium 'moves to the right'
- if the temperature is increased, the equilibrium moves in the endothermic direction

■ ***TIP*** The changes in equilibrium composition are better understood by using the equilibrium constant for changes in concentration or pressure, or the *van't Hoff isochore* for changes in temperature. The change in equilibrium composition on changing the conditions does not return the conditions to their original state; thus, raising the temperature of an equilibrium system causes it to react in the endothermic direction; this does not cool the system, because the higher temperature is the new equilibrium temperature. The different sets of conditions are always equilibrium conditions.

ligand: an atom, ion or molecule that is bonded via a *dative covalent bond* to a metal ion, usually a *transition element* ion.

■ Ligands that join using one pair of electrons are monodentate, those using two are bidentate, and so on.

■ ***e.g.*** Water is the ligand in $[Cu(H_2O)_6]^{2+}$.

■ ***TIP*** The ligand electrons are accepted into vacant orbitals on the metal ion. These are not necessarily the 3*d* orbitals.

ligand exchange: the process where one type of *ligand* in a *complex ion* is replaced by another.

■ ***e.g.*** Water ligands in hexaqua ions can sometimes be replaced by ammonia:

$$[Cu(H_2O)_6]^{2+} + 4NH_3 \longrightarrow [Cu(NH_3)_4(H_2O)_2]^{2+} + 4H_2O$$

line spectrum: if a current is passed through a gas consisting of atoms, such as hydrogen or sodium, the spectrum emitted is found to consist of a series of sharp lines separated by darkness.

■ The lines arise from excited electrons falling back to lower energy levels within the atom. The line spectrum furnished some of the first evidence for clearly defined electron energy levels within atoms.

■ ***TIP*** The line spectrum for sodium has two lines (a doublet) very close together in the yellow region of the spectrum. It is a commonly used source of monochromatic light in the laboratory.

lipid: originally a term meaning any substance that could be dissolved from living material using chloroform, $CHCl_3$ (trichloromethane).

■ As this is such a huge variety of substances, this definition makes the term practically useless as a classification, so it is now more or less synonymous with

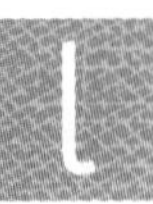

fats, oils and various other fatty materials such as sphingolipids in nerve tissue. It remains a pretty broad set of substances.

liquid: the state of matter characterised by fixed volume but variable shape.

■ There is short range order in liquids — sometimes considerable order in water and in liquid metals — but not the long-range order found in solid crystals.

lithium aluminium hydride, $LiAlH_4$: lithium tetrahydridoaluminate — a powerful reducing agent for polar double bonds such as C=O, C≡N or C=N, but it is without effect on C=C bonds.

■ It is used in dry ethoxyethane, the complex product then being carefully decomposed by addition of dilute ethanoic acid. The reagent effectively acts as the nucleophile H^-.

■ ***e.g.*** Ketones are reduced to secondary alcohols:

$$CH_3COCH_3 + 2[H] \longrightarrow CH_3CH(OH)CH_3$$

■ ***TIP*** The device [H] is commonly used in organic reactions where the intermediate reactions are quite complex and the reducing agent is not hydrogen itself.

lone pair: a pair of electrons not shared by any of the atoms constituting the molecule.

■ Lone pairs affect the shape of a molecule (see *valence shell electron-pair repulsion theory*) and can be used to form *dative covalent bonds* with, for example, hydrogen ions or *transition element* ions. Lone pairs are also important in *nucleophilic addition* and *substitution*.

macromolecule: a very large molecule, usually with a molar mass in the tens of thousands.

■ ***e.g.*** Many polymers and proteins.

malleability: the property shown by most metals of being deformable without breaking.

■ Malleability arises from the relatively non-directional type of bonding found in metallic crystals.

margarine: semi-solid butter substitute, invented by Hippolyte Mège-Mouriés in 1869.

■ Vegetable oils are usually *unsaturated* and *liquid*; margarine is made by partial or complete *reduction*, or *hydrogenation*, of the double bonds in these oils by hydrogen and a nickel catalyst. It can also be made from (deodorised) fish oils or unsaturated animal fats.

■ ***TIP*** In a dietary sense the fat content of margarine is the same as that of butter. Margarine is not a *fat* in the chemical sense of being an ester of propan-1,2,3-triol.

Markovnikov's rule: when HBr reacts with an asymmetric *alkene* $RCH{=}CH_2$, where R is an *alkyl* or an *aryl* group, the major product is that in which the hydrogen atom adds to that carbon already having most hydrogen atoms.

■ The addition is performed in the gas phase or in an inert organic solvent.

■ ***e.g.*** $CH_3CH{=}CH_2 + HBr \longrightarrow CH_3CH(Br)CH_3$

■ ***TIP*** Markovnikov's rule is not an explanation for the orientation of addition. Nor does it necessarily apply to other hydrogen halides or to other polar compounds that add across double bonds. Nor is the major product the only product; the reaction quoted also gives some 1-bromopropane.

mass number: the number of protons plus the number of neutrons in an atom.

mass spectrometer: a device used to measure the mass of ions and to determine molecular structures.

■ A mass spectrometer ionises gaseous atoms or molecules to give positive ions which are then accelerated through a magnetic field. The field deflects the ions

according to the ratio of their mass to their charge. Measurement of this deflection enables the mass of each ion to be determined very accurately. Molecules fragment in a characteristic way in this technique. The fragment ions can then be identified and used as structural evidence for the original compound.

e.g. The mass spectrum of ethanol is shown. The peaks are $CH_3CH_2OH^+$ at 46, $CH_3CH_2O^+$ at 45, CH_2OH^+ at 31, $CH_3CH_2{}^+$ at 29, and CH_3C^+ at 27.

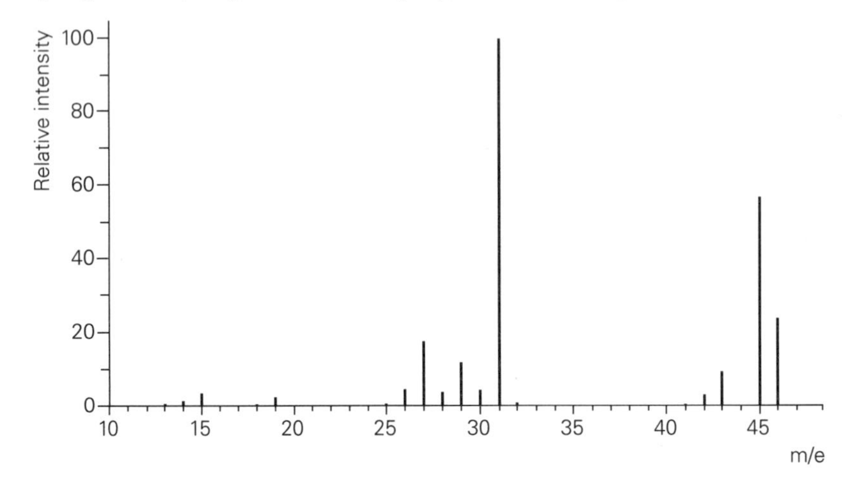

mass spectrum: the output plot from the *mass spectrometer*, which is a bar-graph of abundance against mass/charge ratio, as shown above.

Maxwell–Boltzmann distribution: a graph showing the proportion of molecules in a pure *gas* having a particular speed or a particular energy.

It is often used to explain the effects of a temperature change or the presence of a catalyst on the rate of a chemical reaction. This is not quantitative, as the distribution does not describe mixtures of gases or solutions, where the application of the distribution is even more an act of faith.

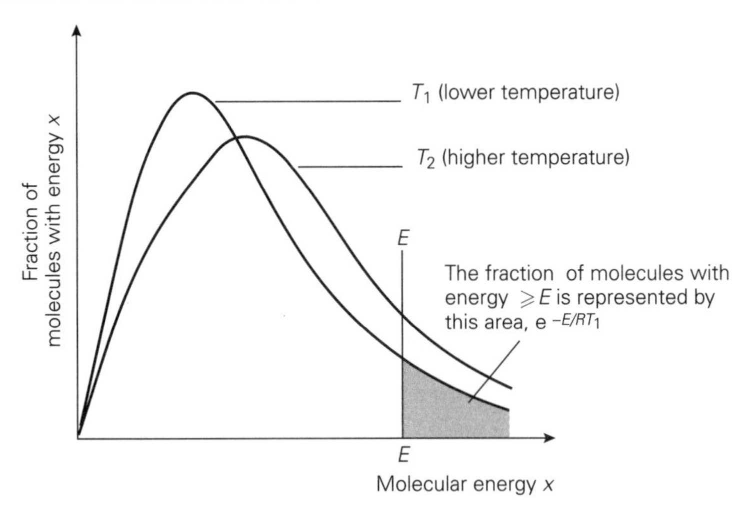

The exemplar distribution above shows the effect of increasing the temperature; the peak shifts to the right but is lower, as the area under the graph is proportional to the amount of gas and is therefore constant. The *activation energy* for a reaction is also shown diagrammatically.

- ***TIP*** The Maxwell–Boltzmann distribution for speed does not have quite the same shape; there is a small initial inflexion.

mean bond enthalpy (also called 'energy')**:** the energy change on breaking a mole of the specified type of bond.

- It can be used to obtain an approximate value for the enthalpy change in a reaction.
- ***TIP*** Mean values may differ substantially from particular values in specific molecules. Thus the mean bond enthalpy for a C=O bond is 743 kJ mol^{-1}, but that for the same bond in carbon dioxide is 805 kJ mol^{-1}.

melting temperature (also called 'melting point')**:** the temperature at which the *liquid* and *solid* forms of a substance are in equilibrium (unless otherwise stated, this is assumed to be at 1 atm pressure).

- A sharp melting temperature indicates a pure substance, except in the special case of a *eutectic*. Substances such as polymers, which contain molecules of many different sizes and therefore differing intermolecular forces, soften over a range of temperature rather than having a sharp melting temperature.
- ***TIP*** The melting temperature and the freezing temperature are the same — which one you use just depends on whether you are melting a solid or cooling a liquid.

membrane cell: a cell used for the *electrolysis* of aqueous sodium chloride to give chlorine, hydrogen and sodium hydroxide.

- The *anode* and *cathode* compartments are separated by an ion-selective membrane, which gives a purer final product than the *diaphragm cell*, of which it is a modification.

metal: an element whose chemistry is dominated by the formation of positive ions, basic or amphoteric oxides, and mostly ionic chlorides.

- All of the *s*-, *d*- and *f*-blocks of the periodic table consist of metallic elements, and eight of the elements of the *p*-block are metals. Metals therefore dominate.

metallic bonding: the type of bonding that exists between metal ions in a *lattice*.

- Metal ions in a lattice are surrounded by free electrons from the outer or *valence shell* of the atom. The metal lattice is usually close-packed, although group 1 metals are not. The mobility of the electrons explains the high electrical conductivity of metals, though not its variation from metal to metal; and the electron 'sea', being relatively non-directional, binds the lattice in any direction and so leads to *malleability* and ductility.

methane, CH_4: the smallest of the *alkanes*, and the main constituent of natural gas and biogas.

methylated spirit: ethanol that has had various impurities added to it to make it undrinkable.

Industrial methylated spirit has 5% of methanol and about 5% of water; mineralised methylated spirit is similar but has a small amount of the pungent wood naphtha and a blue dye added. It is the only variety of methylated spirit or ethanol that can be purchased without Customs and Excise authority.

methyl orange: an *azo dye* that is an acid–base *indicator* — it is red in acid solution and yellow in alkali; the range over which it changes is pH 3.2–4.4.

TIP Methyl orange can be used for strong acid/strong base and strong acid/weak base *titrations*, but for no others (see *titration curves*).

miscible liquid: liquid that mixes in all proportions.

e.g. Hexane and heptane; ethanol and water; gin and tonic.

TIP Some liquids mix in certain proportions but not in others; they are partially miscible. Butanol and water are like this. Others again, such as benzene and water, are almost insoluble in each other and are regarded as immiscible.

molarity: the *concentration* of a solution in mol dm^{-3}.

molar mass: the mass of one mole of substance.

It is numerically equal to the relative molecular or atomic mass of a substance, but has units of g mol^{-1}.

e.g. Sulphuric acid has a relative molecular mass of 98; its molar mass is 98 g mol^{-1}.

molar volume of a gas: one mole of any gas occupies 22.4 dm^3 at 0°C and 1 atm pressure.

TIP Because no essential principle is lost, this is often given as 24 dm^3 'at room temperature and pressure' in exam papers.

mole: one mole of any substance is 6.02×10^{23} particles — ions, atoms, molecules — of it.

The number of moles is the amount of substance.

TIP Indicate clearly what the particles are. Thus 'one mole of iodine' is ambiguous; it should be 'one mole of iodine molecules' or 'one mole of iodine atoms', whichever is appropriate.

molecular covalent structure: a crystal formed by the regular arrangement of molecules into a crystal *lattice*.

e.g. Iodine has a molecular covalent lattice.

TIP Be particularly careful to distinguish *intramolecular bonds* from *intermolecular bonds* in a covalent lattice.

molecular formula: the formula for a molecule, giving the number of each type of atom.

This is often different from the *empirical formula*, which gives the ratio of the atoms present in its lowest terms. Thus the molecular formulae of ethyne,

C_2H_2, cyclobutadiene, C_4H_4, and benzene, C_6H_6, are all different, but they all have the same empirical formula — CH.

molecule: a group of atoms joined by *covalent bonds*; the group may be quite large.

e.g. All the way from hydrogen, H_2, to proteins and enzymes.

mole fraction: applied to a mixture, this is the number of moles of substance divided by the total number of moles in the system:

$$x(\mathrm{A}) = \frac{n(\mathrm{A})}{(n(\mathrm{A}) + n(\mathrm{B}) + \ldots)}$$

The mole fraction is used in the calculation of K_p; the *partial pressure* of a gas is its mole fraction multiplied by the total pressure.

monobasic acid: an acid that has one replaceable hydrogen atom per molecule.

e.g. Hydrochloric acid, HCl; ethanoic acid, CH_3COOH.

monodentate ligand: a *ligand* that bonds to a *transition element* ion using only one pair of electrons.

e.g. Ammonia, $:NH_3$; water, $H_2O:$.

monomer: a small molecule that can be polymerised.

e.g. Ethene, $CH_2{=}CH_2$, polymerises to poly(ethene) $(C_2H_4)_n$.

multiple bond: a bond formed by using more than one pair of electrons.

Multiple bonds always involve one *sigma-bond*, formed by head-to-head overlap of atomic *orbitals*, and one or two *pi-bonds*, formed by sideways overlap of *p*-orbitals.

e.g. C=C, C=O, C=N, C≡C, C≡N.

naphtha: a general term used to describe a light hydrocarbon fraction from *petroleum* distillation with a boiling temperature range between 40° and 150°C.
■ It is used to make other materials, including hydrogen for the *Haber process*.

neutron: the elementary particle having a mass of 1.675×10^{-27} kg and no charge.
■ Neutrons in nuclei are stable; free neutrons (in neutron beams, for example) decay with a *half-life* of about 10 minutes.
■ ***TIP*** The neutron is about 1% more massive than the proton.

nitrating mixture: a mixture of concentrated nitric and sulphuric acids, used to introduce the nitro group, $-NO_2$, into *aromatic* compounds.
■ The mixture produces the *nitronium* or nitryl cation, NO_2^+, via an acid–base reaction in which the nitric acid behaves as a base and accepts a proton from sulphuric acid:

$$H_2SO_4 + HNO_3 \longrightarrow H_2NO_3^+ + HSO_4^-$$
$$H_2NO_3^+ + H_2SO_4 \longrightarrow H_3O^+ + NO_2^+ + HSO_4^-$$

■ ***TIP*** Most aromatic compounds are not very soluble in nitrating mixture, so continuous stirring is necessary to ensure a good yield in the reaction.

nitration: the introduction of a nitro group, $-NO_2$, into an organic compound using *nitrating mixture* or perhaps in some other way.
■ ***e.g.*** Benzene is nitrated at 50°C using nitrating mixture to give nitrobenzene; the temperature must not rise any higher otherwise 1,3-dinitrobenzene is formed in significant amounts:

$$C_6H_6 + HNO_3 \longrightarrow C_6H_5NO_2 + H_2O$$

■ ***TIP*** Unreactive aromatic compounds might need a more vigorous nitrating material, such as fuming (100%) nitric acid; reactive compounds such as phenol or phenylamine can be nitrated using dilute nitric acid.

nitrile: a compound of the form RCN, where R is an *alkyl* or *aryl* group. Nitriles can be *hydrolysed* to *carboxylic acids* or reduced to *primary amines*.

■ ***e.g.*** Methanenitrile, CH_3CN, is the simplest.

■ ***TIP*** The synthesis of a nitrile by the reaction of KCN with a *halogenoalkane* is often used to extend the length of a carbon chain.

nitronium ion, NO_2^+ (also called 'nitryl cation')**:** the ion is formed in *nitrating mixture* and used to nitrate *aromatic* compounds; it is an *electrophile*.

NMR: see *nuclear magnetic resonance (NMR) spectrum*.

noble gases (also called 'inert gases')**:** the elements of group 0 of the periodic table: helium, neon, argon, krypton, xenon, radon.

■ ***TIP*** Although once thought wholly inert, one of the noble gases, xenon, has an extensive chemistry. All xenon compounds contain fluorine or oxygen or both. The first xenon compound XeF_4 was made simply by mixing xenon and fluorine and waiting for a few hours!

nomenclature: the naming of compounds.

■ This can be either systematic, according to *IUPAC* rules, or trivial, according to taste. Systematic names have the advantage of describing the structure of a compound, but they can be very unwieldy for molecules having more than five or so carbon atoms. Trivial names do not tell you anything about structure but are often more fun.

■ ***e.g.*** Folic acid is a vitamin found in liver, green leaves and many other foods. It is still called folic acid by everyone who uses it because its systematic name is six lines long. There is a plant compound called vomitine; its physiological action is clear — its systematic name immense.

non-superimposable mirror image: possession of a non-superimposable mirror image is a necessary and sufficient condition for a molecule to be a *chiral molecule*, and therefore to show *optical activity*.

■ ***e.g.*** Butan-2-ol shows chirality because of the non-superimposable mirror images:

OH, H_3C, C_2H_5, H   OH, H_5C_2, CH_3, H

nuclear magnetic resonance (NMR) spectrum: the spectrum obtained if a hydrogen-containing substance is placed in a very strong magnetic field and then subjected to radio-frequency energy.

■ The radio frequency is absorbed at certain frequencies by the protons. The frequency depends on the environment of the proton, and so an NMR spectrum can be used as part of a structural analysis. NMR can be used to detect other nuclei, not only hydrogen, and hydrogen NMR is more properly called PMR, proton magnetic resonance. However, PMR is so common that it is what is generally understood when NMR is mentioned.

■ ***e.g.*** Benzene, C_6H_6, has only one type of proton, so shows just one peak in the NMR spectrum. Methylbenzene, $C_6H_5CH_3$, has ring protons and methyl group protons and shows two peaks. The horizontal scale is the frequency difference between the absorption and an arbitrary zero, and is in parts per million. This zero is the peak given by the standard reference compound TMS, tetramethylsilane, $Si(CH_3)_4$.

TIP Magnetic resonance imaging (MRI), widely used in medicine to obtain sections through the body non-invasively, is actually three-dimensional NMR. It was originally called 'nuclear magnetic resonance imaging', but 'nuclear' has a poor image with the general public.

Proton NMR spectrum of benzene:

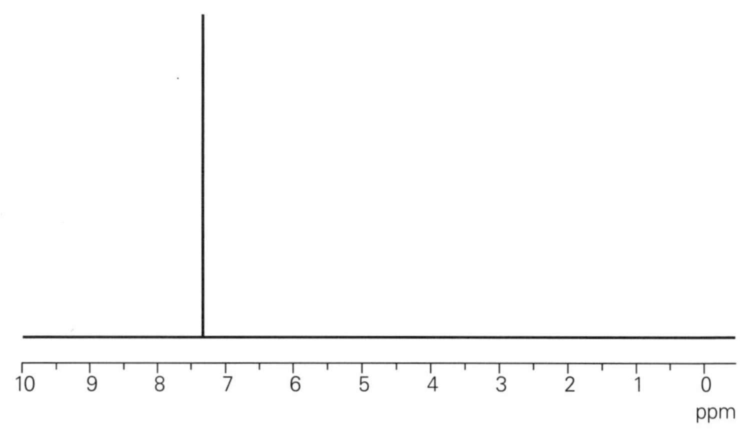

Proton NMR spectrum of methylbenzene; the methyl group protons are at 2.3 ppm:

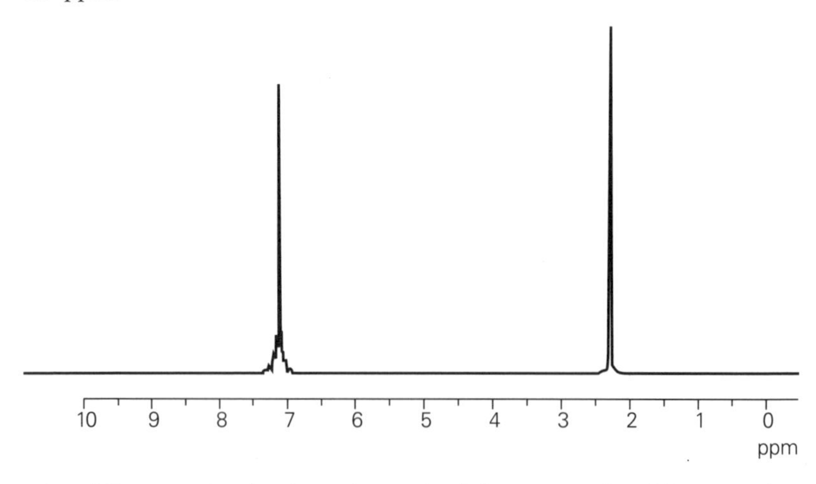

nucleophile: a species that has a *lone pair* of electrons and is able to attack positive regions in other molecules.

e.g. Common nucleophiles are hydroxide, $:OH^-$, cyanide, $:CN^-$, and ammonia, $:NH_3$; there are many others. Nucleophiles react via *substitution reactions*, for example with *halogenoalkanes*, or via *addition reactions* with *carbonyl compounds*.

TIP Always show the lone pair of electrons when writing *reaction mechanisms* involving nucleophiles. Nucleophiles are not necessarily negatively charged.

nucleophilic addition: the reaction between a *nucleophile* and a C=O bond in a *carbonyl* compound.

- The C=O bond is polar (see *polar molecules*), and the nucleophile attacks the carbon atom. Among the most useful nucleophiles in such reactions are the *Grignard reagents*.
- **e.g.** The reaction between propanone and hydrogen cyanide is nucleophilic addition:

$$(H_3C)_2C{=}O + HCN \longrightarrow H_3C\text{–}C(CN)(OH)(CH_3)$$

Propanone is reacted with a solution of potassium cyanide at about pH 8. With the Grignard reagent ethylmagnesium bromide, propanone gives the tertiary alcohol 2-methylbutan-2-ol. The complex initially obtained is treated with dilute hydrochloric acid to liberate the alcohol:

$$(H_3C)_2C{=}O + CH_3CH_2MgBr \longrightarrow H_3C\text{–}C(CH_2CH_3)(OMgBr)(CH_3)$$

$$\xrightarrow{HCl} H_3C\text{–}C(CH_2CH_3)(OH)(CH_3) + Mg^{2+} + Br^- + Cl^-$$

nucleophilic substitution: a reaction where a *nucleophile* replaces another atom or group on the molecule being attacked.

- There are two principal types of nucleophilic substitution mechanism, S_N1 and S_N2.
- **e.g.** The reaction between a *halogenoalkane* and hydroxide ions in aqueous ethanolic solution is nucleophilic substitution:

  S_N1: $(CH_3)_3CBr + OH^- \longrightarrow (CH_3)_3COH + Br^-$

  S_N2: $CH_3Br + OH^- \longrightarrow CH_3OH + Br^-$

nylon: a polyamide that owes its hardness to considerable *hydrogen bonding* between the polymer chains.

- **e.g.** Nylon-6,6 is the best-known structure:

  $...(...CONH(CH_2)_6NHCO(CH_2)_4CONH(CH_2)_6NHCO(CH_2)_4...)...$

- **TIP** Nylon is widely used for manufacturing small precision components such as gear wheels. Many are found in video recorders, for example. It is a very poor insulator at radio frequencies, though it does not conduct otherwise.

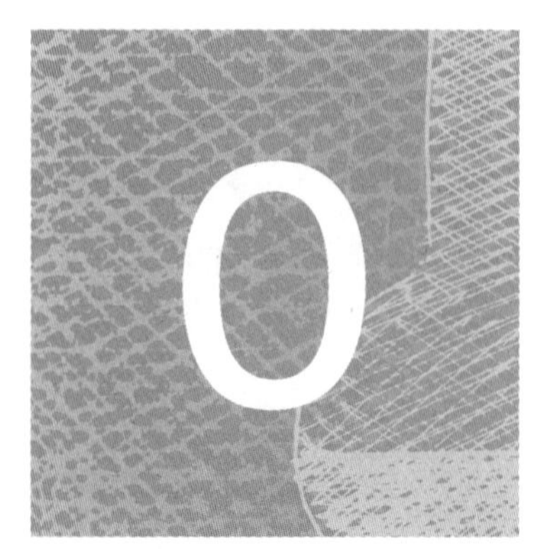

octahedral: molecules or ions that have six bonds to other groups or *ligands*, and no *lone pairs*, are octahedral.

e.g. SF_6; $[Fe(H_2O)_6]^{2+}$; and thousands of other *transition element* complexes:

$$\left[\mathrm{Fe(OH_2)_6}\right]^{2+}$$

TIP When drawing three-dimensional structures, you should show the three-dimensional nature in the way illustrated.

octane number: a number used as a measure of the performance of a motor *fuel*; it is related to the performance of 2,2,4-trimethylpentane, which is also called iso-octane.

A fuel that behaves in the same way as 2,2,4-trimethylpentane is given an octane number of 100. The octane number is related to the ease with which a fuel auto-ignites in an engine: that is, without the help of a spark plug. Heptane auto-ignites easily and has an octane number of 0. Fuel is blended from a variety of straight and *branched chain* compounds, together with *aromatic* compounds, to give a research octane number (RON) appropriate to the engine design. Standard unleaded fuel has RON 95. Aromatic compounds have high RONs; methylbenzene is 120, for example. Straight-chain alkanes tend to have low RONs; hexane is 25.

optical activity: a characteristic of *chiral molecules* whereby they are able to rotate the plane of polarisation of monochromatic *plane-polarised light* shone through them.

Compounds that rotate the plane to the right are dextrorotatory; those that rotate it to the left are laevorotatory. The rotation varies with the wavelength of the light — hence the use of monochromatic light. Sodium light is standard.

e.g. Glucose has several chiral centres, but their net effect rotates light to the right; it is therefore called (+)-glucose.

■ **TIP** The plane is rotated; not bent, twisted, or anything else.

optical isomerism: isomerism arising from molecules having non-superimposable mirror images, i.e. being *chiral*.

■ Such molecules rotate plane-polarised light — see *optical activity*.

orbital: a picture that shows the location of an electron within an atom or, perhaps rather casually, the volume of space that possesses the property of 'electron-ness'.

■ *Covalent bonding* is represented as the overlap of atomic orbitals.

■ **e.g.** Orbitals are classified according to their subshell: *s* (one orbital), *p* (three), *d* (five), and *f* (seven). These orbitals represent (are, in fact) a maximum of 2, 6, 10 and 14 electrons, respectively.

order of reaction: the quantitative description of the effect of *concentration* change on the rate of a chemical reaction is of the form

$$\text{rate} = k[A]^a\ [B]^b...$$

where [A] and [B] represent the concentrations of those species, and k is the rate constant. The powers a and b are the orders of reaction with respect to each reactant, the overall order being $a + b$.

■ The order is significant for the mechanism of the reaction, because it gives the number of each species that is involved up to and including the *rate-determining step* of the reaction. The order can only be determined experimentally; it cannot be inferred from the *stoichiometric* equation for the reaction as this gives no information about the mechanism.

■ **e.g.** A first-order reaction is the *nucleophilic substitution* between 2-bromo-2-methylpropane and hydroxide ions:

$$(CH_3)_3CBr + OH^- \longrightarrow (CH_3)_3COH + Br^-$$

$$\text{rate} = k[(CH_3)_3CBr]$$

A second-order reaction is that between propanone and iodine in acidic solution to give monoiodopropanone:

$$CH_3COCH_3 + I_2 \xrightarrow{H^+} CH_3COCH_2I + HI$$

$$\text{rate} = k[CH_3COCH_3][H^+]$$

organic chemistry: the chemistry of carbon compounds other than that of carbonates and, oddly, of carbon dioxide, CO_2, from which of course all organic compounds ultimately come.

oxidation: the loss of electrons.

■ This leads to an increase in the *oxidation number* (or *oxidation state*) of the atom oxidised.

■ **e.g.** In the reaction of chlorine with bromide ions in seawater, the bromide ions lose electrons and are oxidised. The oxidation state goes from (–1) to (0):

$$2Br^-(aq) + Cl_2(aq) \longrightarrow Br_2(aq) + 2Cl^-(aq)$$

oxidation number, oxidation state: the difference between the number of

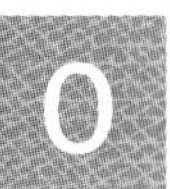

electrons associated with an element in a compound and the element itself.

In some ways, assigning oxidation numbers is an electronic book-keeping exercise, where all compounds are regarded as being made up of ions, irrespective of the actual nature of the bonding. Atoms are oxidised if their oxidation number rises and reduced if it falls. The oxidation number of combined oxygen is usually (–2) (except in *peroxides* and *superoxides*), that of combined fluorine is always (–1), and that of simple monatomic ions is the same as the ionic charge. Combined hydrogen is (+1) except in the *hydrides* of groups 1 and 2 (e.g. LiH), where it is (–1).

e.g. The oxidation number of Mn in the ion MnO_4^- is found thus: $[Mn^{x+}(O^{2-})_4]^-$ assumes all-ionic bonding; thus $x = +7$. This ion in acidic solution reacts with a wide variety of substances and produces Mn^{2+}; the MnO_4^- ion has been reduced.

TIP The terms 'oxidation number' and 'oxidation state' are used virtually interchangeably; an atom has a particular oxidation number or is described as being in a particular oxidation state.

oxide: a compound of oxygen with another element where the oxygen has the *oxidation number* (–2).

e.g. Na_2O, MgO, Al_2O_3, SiO_2, P_4O_{10}, Cl_2O.

TIP Beware formulae that look like oxides but aren't. Thus PbO_2 is an oxide, but BaO_2 is not, as the oxygen-containing ion is *peroxide*, O_2^{2-}.

oxidising agent: a reagent that brings about *oxidation*, being itself reduced in the process (see *reduction*).

e.g. O_2, Cl_2, MnO_4^-, $Cr_2O_7^{2-}$, PbO_2.

oxo-acid: an acidic compound that contains oxygen.

e.g. H_2SO_4, HNO_3, $HClO_3$, and many others.

oxo-anion: an anion that contains oxygen.

It is the *conjugate base* of the oxo-acid.

e.g. SO_4^{2-}, NO_3^-, ClO_3^-.

oxo-cation: a *cation* containing oxygen.

e.g. VO^{2+}, VO^+.

oxonium ion: a positively charged ion that contains oxygen.

e.g. The *hydroxonium ion*, H_3O^+, is the best-known.

ozonolysis: a technique for finding the position of a C=C double bond in an alkene.

The alkene is reacted with ozone-enriched oxygen and the intermediate ozonide is reacted with dilute ethanoic acid in the presence of powdered zinc. This results in *carbonyl compounds*, which can be isolated and identified.

$$(a)(b)C{=}C(d)(e) \longrightarrow (a)(b)C{=}O \quad O{=}C(d)(e)$$

paramagnetism: the property shown by *transition element* ions, or molecules that have unpaired electrons, of being repelled by a magnetic field.

■ ***TIP*** Oxygen is paramagnetic; it cannot, therefore, have a true double bond between the atoms because this would lead to pairing of all the electrons.

partial pressure: the pressure that would be exerted by a single *gas* in a gas mixture if it alone were to occupy the same volume as the mixture at the same temperature and pressure.

■ It is equal to the *mole fraction* of the gas multiplied by the total pressure.

■ ***e.g.*** The mole fraction of oxygen in the air is about 0.2; thus its partial pressure at a total pressure of 1 atm is 0.2 atm.

■ ***TIP*** Partial pressures are used most often in the calculation of K_p, the *equilibrium constant*, in terms of pressure.

partition law: if a substance that is soluble in two immiscible liquids is shaken with the liquids until *equilibrium* is achieved, the ratio of the *solute* concentration in the two *solvents* is constant at constant temperature:

$$\frac{\text{concentration of X in solvent 1}}{\text{concentration of X in solvent 2}} = D$$

where D is called the partition coefficient or the distribution coefficient.

■ ***TIP*** The value of D depends on the solvents, the solute and the temperature.

Pauli exclusion principle: the principle that no two electrons in a given atom can have all four *quantum numbers* the same.

p-block element: an element where the valence electrons are in the p-shell (see *valence shell*).

■ These elements are those in groups 3 to 7, and 0.

percentage yield: if the amount of material expected from a reaction is calculated assuming no losses, and the actual amount obtained is measured, then the percentage yield is

$$\%\ \text{yield} = \frac{\text{amount obtained}}{\text{amount expected}} \times 100$$

■ A knowledge of yield is crucial in multi-stage synthetic processes. Eighty

per cent represents a good yield for many organic reactions; two of these in succession gives 64% overall, and three in succession gives just over 50%. This is why any synthetic pathway should use the minimum possible number of steps.

period: a horizontal division of the *periodic table.*

■ Periods begin with an alkali metal and end with a noble gas (see also *group*).

periodic table: the periodic table currently in use is essentially that of Dmitri Ivanovitch Mendeleev, which was published in 1869 but drew on the previous attempts of Döbereiner and Newlands to classify the elements.

■ The greatness of Mendeleev's table lies partly in the fact that it enabled the prediction of unknown elements. The most famous example is that of eka-silicon or germanium. Germanium was discovered in 1886, yet Mendeleev had predicted many of the physical and chemical properties of the element, its oxides and its chlorides with astonishing accuracy in 1871. The elements, arranged in order of their atomic number, show properties that recur at certain fixed intervals. This leads to the existence of groups. The original version of the Mendeleev table is carved on his memorial in St Petersburg.

permanent dipole: a separation of charge in bonds between atoms of different *electronegativity.*

■ Thus C–Cl bonds are polar, with the chlorine being the more negative end of the dipole. Polar bonds will lead to molecules that are polar overall (e.g. ammonia, NH_3) if the contributions of the individual dipoles do not cancel. However, molecules such as tetrachloromethane, CCl_4, have bonds that are polar but molecules that are not, as the individual dipoles do cancel.

Ammonia | Tetrachloromethane

peroxide: a compound containing the ion O_2^{2-}; peroxides are formally salts of hydrogen peroxide, H_2O_2.

■ ***e.g.*** Sodium, on burning in air, forms mostly sodium peroxide, Na_2O_2:

$$2Na(s) + O_2(g) \longrightarrow Na_2O_2(s)$$

■ ***TIP*** Peroxides are not always obvious from the formula — you need to look at the oxidation state of the other ion present. Thus BaO_2 is a peroxide with Ba^{2+} and O_2^{2-}; PbO_2 is not, having Pb^{4+} and O^{2-}; neither is KO_2 with K^+ and O_2^-.

pesticide: a substance designed to kill animal pests.

■ DDT is one of the best-known and one of the most notorious. Despite its problems, its use against mosquitoes has successfully eradicated malaria from many parts of the world formerly plagued by this serious disease.

pH: a measure of the acidity or alkalinity of a solution; it is defined as pH = $-\log([H^+]/\text{mol dm}^{-3})$.

■ ***TIP*** The division of the *concentration* by the unit is necessary because the logarithm of a physical quantity is meaningless; only the logarithm of a number is meaningful. The limits to pH are defined by the most concentrated strong acid and the most concentrated strong base obtainable and, in practice, are roughly −1.5 to 15.

phase: a homogeneous part of a chemical system within a distinct boundary.

■ ***e.g.*** A stoppered flask containing a single liquid and its vapour contains two phases, one the liquid and the other the vapour. A similar flask containing oil and water has three phases; the oil and water are immiscible and form two liquid phases in addition to the gas phase.

■ ***TIP*** In a *homogeneous equilibrium* the reactants and products are in the same phase, not the same *state*. A mixture of immiscible liquids is not homogeneous even though the states are the same.

phenol: a compound having an –OH group attached to an *aromatic* ring.

■ ***e.g.*** The compound actually called phenol, C_6H_5OH, has antiseptic properties and was used in the first operations by Lister to reduce the risk of death from septicaemia.

phenolphthalein: a common acid–base *indicator*, used for strong acid/strong base and weak acid/strong base *titrations*.

■ Its colour changes over a pH range of 8.3–10.0. It is colourless in acid solution, magenta in alkaline solution.

■ ***TIP*** If the alkali is run in from the burette, the endpoint is the volume when the solution turns permanently pink. If left, the colour will disappear owing to absorption of carbon dioxide from the atmosphere by the alkaline solution. No more alkali should be added to counteract this drift; the titration's reaction has finished.

phenyl: the group C_6H_5–.

■ ***TIP*** Distinguish clearly phenyl from the compound phenol C_6H_5OH.

pH meter: an *electrochemical cell* where the potential of one of the electrodes is sensitive to the pH of the solution in which it is placed.

■ The cell is engineered as a single probe that can be dipped into the solution of interest, and the meter is actually a voltmeter.

photochemical reaction: a reaction initiated by light.

■ ***e.g.*** The photohalogenation of methane by chlorine to give chloromethane, CH_3Cl, which requires ultraviolet light to split the chlorine molecules via *homolytic fission* into *radicals*:

$$Cl_2 \longrightarrow 2Cl\bullet$$

pi-bond (also written as 'π-bond')**:** a bond arising from the sideways overlap of *p-orbitals*.

■ All multiply bonded atoms have one (double bonds) or two (triple bonds) pi-bonds between them.

pK_a: pK_a = –logK_a. (See also K_a.)

pK_w: pK_w = –logK_w. (See also K_w.)

plane-polarised light: light which has been passed through a polariser so that the electric component of the electromagnetic wave vibrates in one plane only.

■ It is used in the detection of *optical activity*.

■ ***TIP*** Plane-polarised sodium light is used for detection of optical activity, because it is virtually monochromatic and optical rotation varies with wavelength.

plastic: as an adjective, this means 'deformable'; as a noun, it refers to a whole variety of *polymers*, both addition and condensation. It is not a precise scientific term.

■ ***TIP*** In the early days of polymer use, it was common to find that the wrong variety of polymer was employed. Plastic items had a reputation for cheap tawdriness, so the word was sometimes used pejoratively. Many intricate items now available cheaply and in quantity could not be made as well or as accurately using other materials. The ready availability of precision *nylon* gears is an example in point.

polarisability: the extent to which the electron distribution in a molecule, ion or an atom can be distorted by an externally applied electric field.

■ It is important when considering bonding interactions.

■ ***e.g.*** The ion Mg^{2+} has quite a high *charge density* and is therefore polarising; when combined with iodide ions, the magnesium ion distorts the electron cloud of the iodide ion so that the bonding in MgI_2 has significant covalent character. The iodide ion is large, the electrons are not held very tightly, and it is therefore polarisable. The fluoride ion is much smaller, much less subject to distortion, and MgF_2 is ionic.

polarity: the dipole possessed by a bond in consequence of *electronegativity* differences in the bonded atoms. (See *permanent dipole*.)

polar molecule: a molecule that rotates when placed in an electric field because the electrons are not equally distributed in the bonds owing to *electronegativity* differences between the bonded atoms.

■ Not all polar bonds give rise to polar molecules. (See *permanent dipole* for examples.)

poly(amide): a *condensation polymer* where the monomer groups are linked by an amide group –CONH–.

■ ***e.g.*** Nylon-6,6 is the best-known synthetic poly(amide):

$$...(...CONH(CH_2)_6NHCO(CH_2)_4CONH(CH_2)_6NHCO(CH_2)_4...)...$$

poly(ester): a *condensation polymer* where the linkages between the monomers are ester links.

■ *e.g.* Terylene, which has the structure

$$\left[-\overset{\displaystyle O}{\overset{\|}{C}}-C_6H_4-\overset{\displaystyle O}{\overset{\|}{C}}-OCH_2CO- \right]_n$$

polymer: a long-chain molecule formed by *addition* or *condensation reactions*.

■ *e.g.* Addition polymers include poly(ethene), poly(propene), poly(styrene); condensation polymers include *nylon* and *poly(esters)*.

***p*-orbital:** an atomic orbital with the shape shown below.

■ There are three of them, one along each of the three axes, for every shell from the second onwards.

precipitation reaction (also called 'double decomposition')**:** the reaction of two soluble salts to give one soluble and one insoluble salt.

■ Such reactions are often used in qualitative analysis.

■ *e.g.* The test for sulphate ions uses the insolubility of barium sulphate as its basis:

$$Ba^{2+}(aq) + SO_4^{2-}(aq) \longrightarrow BaSO_4(s)$$

It does not matter what the sulphate is as long as it is soluble in water. Barium chloride or barium nitrate can be used as the test reagent since both are soluble.

■ ***TIP*** Use the name 'precipitation reaction' rather than 'double decomposition'.

primary alcohol: an *alcohol* containing the $-CH_2OH$ group.

■ *e.g.* Ethanol, CH_3CH_2OH, benzyl alcohol, $C_6H_5CH_2OH$.

primary amine: an amine of the form RNH_2, where R is an *alkyl* or *aryl* group.

■ *e.g.* Methylamine, CH_3NH_2, phenylamine, $C_6H_5NH_2$.

promoter: a substance added to a *catalyst* to enhance its effectiveness, though the substance is not itself a catalyst for the reaction.

■ *e.g.* The iron catalyst used in the *Haber process* for the synthesis of ammonia from nitrogen and hydrogen has promoters of aluminium oxide and potassium oxide.

protein: a *poly(amide)* composed of the 20 naturally occurring *amino acids* in a specific order depending on the particular protein.

proton: the elementary particle found in the nucleus and having a mass of 1.673×10^{-27} kg and a charge of $+1.6 \times 10^{-19}$ C.

proton magnetic resonance (PMR): *nuclear magnetic resonance* as applied to protons.

As the majority of NMR is also PMR, the two terms are sometimes regarded, however inaccurately, as synonymous.

pyramidal: the molecular shape formed by substances that have *lone pairs* of electrons, which according to *valence shell electron-pair repulsion theory* are stereochemically important.

e.g. Ammonia forms a triangular pyramid; four pairs of electrons give a tetrahedral arrangement, but one is a lone pair and so the molecule's shape is a pyramid:

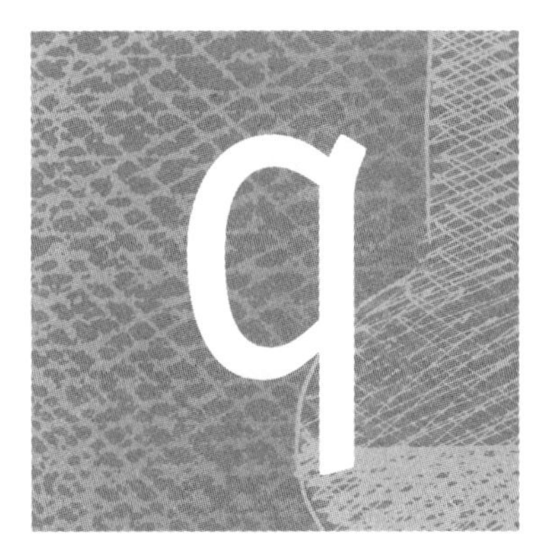

qualitative analysis: analysis to determine the nature of the constituents of a material.

quantitative analysis: analysis to determine the amount of each constituent in a material.

quantum: the parcel of energy of particular size associated with electromagnetic radiation.

- The minimum amount of radiation that can be transferred is one quantum, which for radiation of frequency f is given by $E = hf$, where h is Planck's constant.

quantum number (for electrons): the quantum theory of the atom assigns each electron four quantum numbers.

- These specify which shell, which subshell, which orbital in the subshell, and which electron in the orbital, a particular electron is. The four numbers are:
  - principal quantum number n; this defines the shell, and takes values 1, 2, 3...
  - subsidiary quantum number; this defines the subshell, and takes values 0, 1,...n–1. s-orbitals have $l = 0$, p-orbitals $l = 1$, d-orbitals $l = 2$
  - magnetic quantum number m; this defines which orbital the electron is in, and takes values 0, ±1, ... $\pm l$
  - spin quantum number s; this takes values $\pm{}^1/_2$.

  The *Pauli exclusion principle* states that no two electrons in an atom can have the same four quantum numbers.

quantum shell: the energy that electrons possess in an atom is quantised; that is, it can have only certain values.

- The model of the atom due to Bohr that showed orbiting electrons at particular distances from the nucleus, i.e. in shells, means in modern terms that the electrons occupy energy levels that can have only certain values.

racemic mixture: an equimolar mixture of the two mirror-image forms of a chiral compound.

- As their rotation of *plane-polarised light* is equal but opposite, the mixture is not optically active. Racemic mixtures are the usual product when *chiral compounds* are formed in chemical reactions, unless a stereo-specific synthesis can be devised.
- ***e.g.*** In the S_N1 reaction of 2-bromobutane with hydroxide ions to give butan-2-ol, the intermediate is a planar carbocation. This can be attacked with equal probability from either side by $:OH^-$, so the product is a mixture of the (+) and (–) isomers of butan-2-ol. (In this reaction there is also some S_N2, so the product is not completely racemic.)

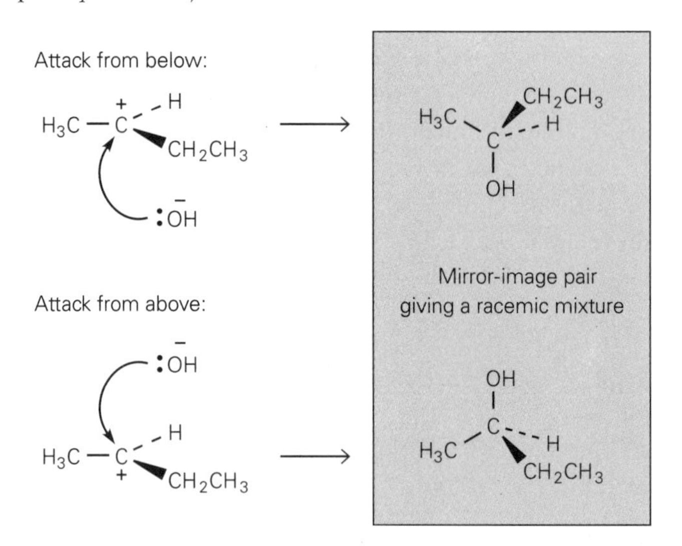

radiation: the transmission of energy by means of an electromagnetic wave; or the emission of particles from the nucleus of a radioactive nuclide.

- ***e.g.*** Electromagnetic waves have frequencies from 10 kHz (wavelength of 30 000 m) to 3×10^{14} MHz (wavelength of 10^{-12} m). The orders of magnitudes

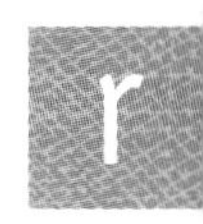

of the various parts of the electromagnetic spectrum are shown in the table below.

Radiation	λ/m	f/MHz	Energy = hf/kJ mol^{-1}
Gamma rays	10^{-12}	3×10^{14}	1.2×10^{8}
X-rays	10^{-10}	3×10^{12}	1.2×10^{6}
UV	10^{-8}	3×10^{10}	1.2×10^{4}
Visible	10^{-6}	3×10^{8}	1.2×10^{2}
IR	10^{-4}	3×10^{6}	1.2
Microwaves	10^{-2}	3×10^{4}	1.2×10^{-2}
UHF (TV)	1	3×10^{2}	1.2×10^{-4}
HF (short wave)	10^{2}	3	1.2×10^{-6}

radical: a species having a lone electron.

- Radicals are usually very reactive and often indiscriminate in where they attack other molecules. They are important intermediates in photohalogenation of *alkanes*, as well as in addition polymerisation. Radical reactions often need to be initiated by the presence of light or *peroxides*.
- ***e.g.*** The halogenation of methane by chlorine has as its first step the *homolytic fission* of the chlorine molecule by ultraviolet light into two chlorine atoms. As these have lone electrons, they are radicals:

  $$Cl{:}Cl \longrightarrow 2Cl\bullet$$
- ***TIP*** There are some radicals which are quite stable; one of the best-known is triphenylmethyl, $(C_6H_5)_3C\bullet$, which is stable as a pale yellow solution in hexane or benzene if air is excluded.

radioactivity: the phenomenon of nuclear decay leading to the emission of α, β or γ radiation, and also that of spontaneous fission by nuclides such as uranium into two or more smaller fragments.

- The element changes during radioactive decay — the alchemists would have been pleased. All elements have radioactive isotopes; $_{43}Tc$, $_{61}Pm$ and $_{84}Po$, together with all the elements beyond 84, have only radioactive isotopes. Natural radioactivity constitutes some 87% of the radiation humans receive; a further 11.5% is from medical sources. Nuclear emissions from man's activities, e.g. nuclear power, account for only 0.1%.
- ***e.g.*** Carbon-14 has a nucleus with too many neutrons for it to be stable. A neutron is converted to a proton and an electron, which is emitted as a β-particle. The atom remaining is now nitrogen:

  $$^{14}_{6}C \longrightarrow {}^{14}_{7}N + {}^{0}_{-1}\beta$$

rate constant: the constant of proportionality *k* in the *rate equation*.

- The rate constant is specific to a particular reaction, and varies with temperature. Determining the rate constant at two different temperatures enables

the calculation of the *activation energy* for the reaction using the *van't Hoff isochore.*

rate-determining (or limiting) step: the slowest part of the *reaction mechanism,* which will determine the overall reaction *rate.*

The reagents that appear in the rate equation are those that are involved in the mechanism up to and including the rate-determining step.

e.g. In the S_N2 reaction of bromomethane with hydroxide ions, both of these substances are involved in the rate-determining step which is the only step in the reaction:

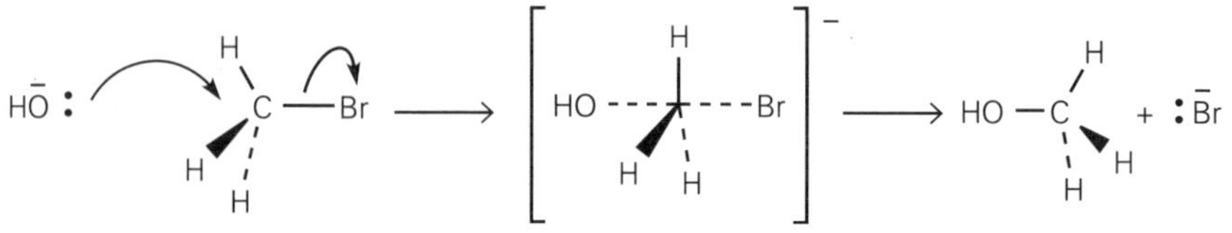

The S_N1 reaction of 2-bromo-2-methylpropane with hydroxide ions is a two-step reaction, the first of which is the rate-determining step:

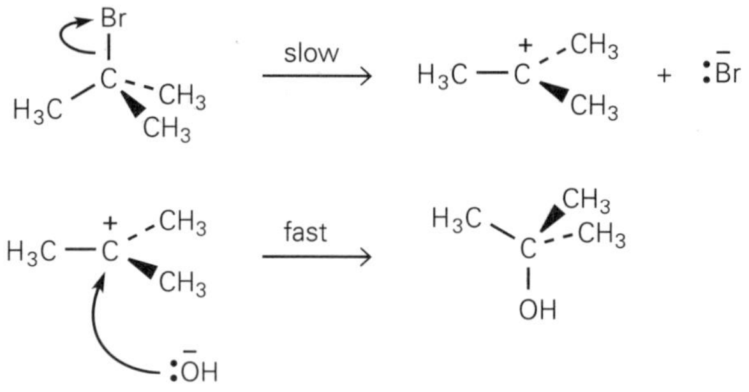

rate equation: the equation that relates the rate of a reaction to the concentrations of the reagents.

It is not related to the *stoichiometric equation* for the reaction, but is dependent on the *reaction mechanism.* All rate equations have to be determined experimentally.

e.g. The rate equation for the S_N2 reaction between bromomethane and hydroxide ions in aqueous ethanolic solution

$$CH_3Br + OH^- \longrightarrow CH_3OH + Br^-$$

is

$$\text{rate} = k[CH_3Br]\,[OH^-]$$

rate of reaction: the rate of change of concentration of reactants or of products in a reaction. The rate has units of mol dm^{-3} s^{-1}.

reaction mechanism: a representation of the changes in electronic structure that occur during a reaction.

The movement of electron pairs is shown by means of *curly arrows.* Mechanisms are most common for organic reactions, but can equally well be written for inorganic reactions where covalent bonding is involved. Reaction kinetics provides much of the evidence on which mechanistic studies rest. (See also *nucleophilic addition, nucleophilic substitution, electrophilic substitution, S_N2.*)

- ***e.g.*** The S_N1 reaction of 2-bromo-2-methylpropane with hydroxide ions in aqueous ethanol is shown:

- ***TIP*** Attack on the planar carbocation can be from above or below; this is important if the starting halogenoalkane is chiral. (See *racemic mixture*.)

reaction profile: an *enthalpy level diagram* that represents the energy changes that occur as a reaction proceeds.

- Commonly depicted as a single-humped pathway to show the activation energy (below, first diagram); multi-step reactions have a hump for each step (below, second diagram).
- ***TIP*** The activated complex is not an intermediate. The complex is a transitional structure at a high energy peak; an intermediate is in an energy trough (see second diagram) and has a significant lifetime.

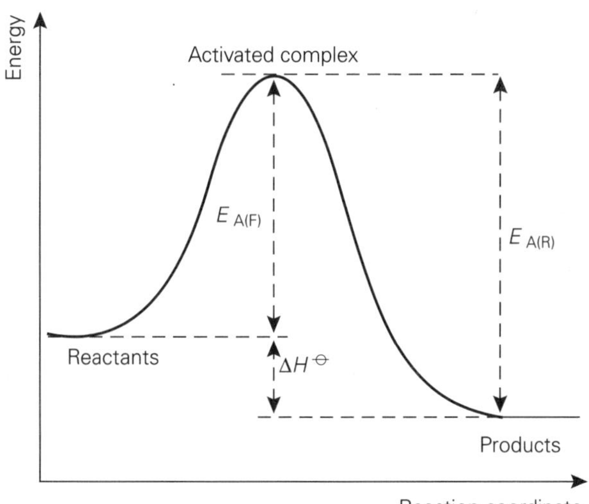

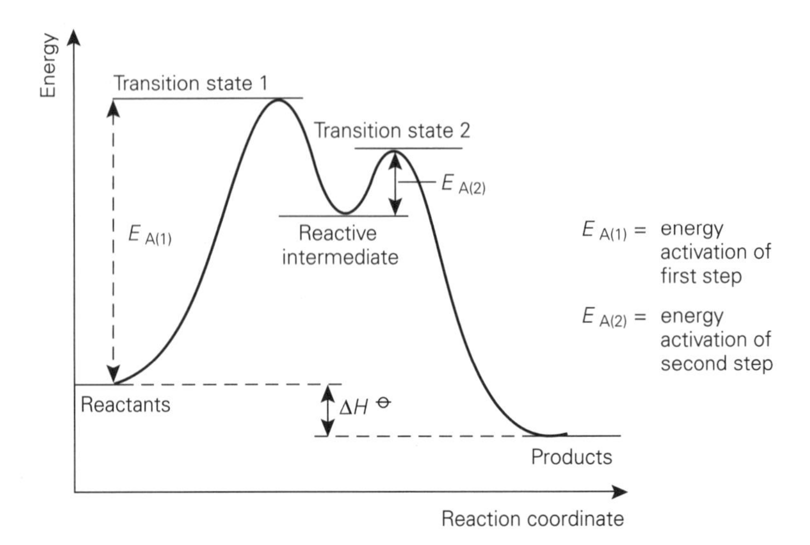

reagent (also called 'reactant')**:** one of the starting materials for a chemical reaction.

■ ***TIP*** Always give reagent names in full in formal writing, which includes examinations. Thus, rather than 'acidified dichromate' as an oxidising agent for *alcohols*, you should write 'potassium dichromate and dilute sulphuric acid'.

recrystallisation: a technique of purification of solid substances.

■ The solid is dissolved in the minimum amount of boiling *solvent*, filtered to remove solids if necessary, and then cooled. The crystals are filtered, washed with a small amount of cold solvent, and then dried. The basis of the technique is that at the *boiling temperature* the solution is saturated with respect to the main material, but not with respect to impurities. These do not therefore crystallise. The choice of a suitable solvent is important; the difference in *solubility* at the boiling temperature and at room temperature (or that of the fridge) should be as large as possible to avoid unacceptable losses.

redox reaction (also called 'electron transfer reaction')**:** shorthand for oxidation–reduction reaction.

reducing agent: the substance that donates electrons in a *redox reaction*, and is therefore itself oxidised.

■ ***e.g.*** In the reaction of chlorine with bromide ions (used to produce bromine from *seawater*) the bromide ions donate electrons to the chlorine atoms, and therefore bromide is the reducing agent:

$$2Br^-(aq) + Cl_2(aq) \longrightarrow Br_2(aq) + 2Cl^-(aq)$$

reduction: the addition of electrons to a substance — as with the chlorine in the example above.

reduction potential, standard: the potential difference that is obtained when

a given electrode is combined in an *electrochemical cell* with the *standard hydrogen electrode* is called the reduction potential of the electrode.

- It is quoted in tables for the process of electron addition, that is *reduction*.
- ***e.g.*** $Cu^{2+} + 2e^- \rightleftharpoons Cu$ $E^\ominus = +0.34$ V

  $MnO_4^- + 8H^+ + 5e^- \rightleftharpoons Mn^{2+} + 4H_2O$ $E^\ominus = +1.52$ V

reflux: liquid that has vaporised from a reaction mixture and is condensed (see *condensation*) and returned to the mixture.

- Generally this is achieved by means of a vertical Liebig condenser above the mixture.
- ***TIP*** 'Reflux' is often used as a verb to mean 'heat under reflux'. If you mean 'heat under reflux', say so. A reflux condenser is sometimes employed when the mixture is not being boiled. An example is in the *nitration* of benzene with *nitrating mixture*, where the temperature should not rise above 50°C.

reforming: changing the structure of an organic compound, usually in order to improve the *octane number* of fuels. (See also *steam reforming*.)

- The changes usually involve converting straight-chain compounds into branched-chain ones.

relative atomic mass: the average mass of an element compared with the mass of one-twelfth of a ^{12}C atom.

- This average mass refers to the naturally occurring mixture of *isotopes* of the element concerned. It has no units because it is a ratio.
- ***e.g.*** Naturally occurring chlorine consists of 75% ^{35}Cl and 25% ^{37}Cl; the relative atomic mass of chlorine is therefore:

  $(0.75 \times 35) + (0.25 \times 37) = 35.5$.
- ***TIP*** The isotopic composition of an element is not necessarily constant from place to place; there is small variation depending on the source of the element, this being one of the problems associated with the original scales of relative atomic mass that were based on hydrogen or oxygen. Note that a given atom cannot have a *mass number* of 35.5 because you cannot have half a neutron or half a proton.

relative isotopic mass: the mass of a particular *isotope* of an element compared with the mass of one-twelfth of a ^{12}C atom.

- It has no units because it is a ratio.
- ***e.g.*** The relative isotopic mass of ^{12}C is defined as 12 units exactly.
- ***TIP*** Relative isotopic masses can be found to a very high degree of precision by the *mass spectrometer*, the tool originally used by F. W. Aston to show the existence of isotopes in neon and for which he won the Nobel prize.

repeating unit: the unit of a *polymer* chain that originates from a single *monomer* molecule, in the case of addition polymers, or from the pair of molecules usually used to make condensation polymers.

In poly(alkenes) the repeating unit has the same number of carbon atoms as the monomer, i.e. the original alkene. In condensation polymers such as nylon or poly(esters) the repeating unit is a combination of the two monomers used to make the polymer.

e.g. Poly(ethene) has the repeating unit ...(–CH_2–CH_2–)... Nylon-6,6 is made from $ClOC(CH_2)_4COCl$ and $H_2N(CH_2)_6NH_2$; the repeating unit therefore being ...(...$OC(CH_2)_4COHN(CH_2)_6NH$...)...

restricted rotation: the phenomenon where bonded atoms cannot rotate relative to one another because either the bond between them prevents it or because the two atoms are part of a ring that restricts rotation.

Restricted rotation gives rise to some forms of *geometric isomerism*.

e.g. C=C bonds have restricted rotation because of the sideways overlap of the *p-orbitals* that gives the π-bond:

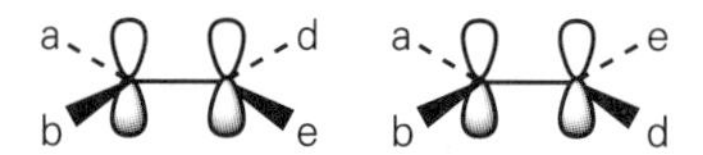

1,2-Dichlorocyclohexane has two isomers because the ring prevents rotation about the single C–C bond:

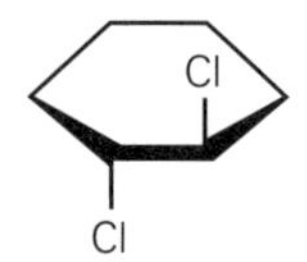

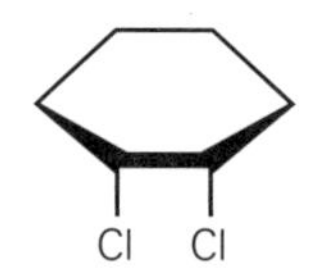

(Note that the cyclohexene ring is not flat as shown here; it is chair-shaped.)

reversible reaction: a reaction that can proceed in either direction as conventionally written in an equation.

Where a reversible reaction has equal forward and reverse rates, so that there is no net change in composition, the reaction is in *equilibrium*.

e.g. The esterification of ethanoic acid with ethanol is reversible (as is the acid *hydrolysis* of the ester):

$$CH_3COOH + CH_3CH_2OH \rightleftharpoons CH_3COOCH_2CH_3 + H_2O$$

TIP Some chemists will say that all reactions are reversible in principle; perhaps they have never studied explosions!

risk assessment: chemistry involves handling materials that are hazardous, so any experiment must have a risk assessment made to ensure that the *hazards* have been recognised and that proper facilities, such as fume cupboards, are used where necessary.

The purpose of a risk assessment is not to prevent experiments, but to educate in the responsible handling of possibly dangerous materials.

salt bridge: the two electrodes of an *electrochemical cell* have their solutions connected by a salt bridge, which brings the solutions to the same electrical potential.

- A solution of potassium chloride is used, unless one of the electrodes contains lead or silver ions, in which case potassium nitrate is used.
- ***TIP*** The salt bridge is used in a cell that is not designed to deliver current; no ions pass through the bridge if no current is drawn, which is the proper state for a cell where the e.m.f. is to be accurately measured.

salting out: increasing the yield of an organic compound from solution by the addition of sodium chloride.

- Some organic substances are appreciably soluble in water but much less so in concentrated solutions of sodium chloride. Addition of NaCl can therefore be used to increase the yield in a synthesis where an aqueous/organic system is produced.
- ***e.g.*** Two substances that can be salted out are phenylamine and methyl orange.

saturated compound: an organic compound that contains no double or triple bonds, and which therefore reacts only by *substitution reactions*.

- ***e.g.*** *Alkanes* are the simplest example.

saturated solution: a *solution* which cannot dissolve any more of a particular *solute*.

- Such solutions will deposit crystals of the solute on cooling or *evaporation*. The aim in *recrystallisation* is to produce a saturated solution of the material to be purified at the boiling temperature of the solvent.

saturated vapour pressure: a liquid in a sealed container will evaporate until the vapour and the liquid are in equilibrium; the vapour pressure exerted under these conditions at any stated constant temperature is the saturated vapour pressure at that temperature.

- ***TIP*** If the saturated vapour pressure of a liquid is equal to atmospheric pressure, then the temperature is, by definition, the *boiling temperature* of the liquid.

s-block elements: elements where the valence electrons are in an *s-orbital.*

■ They are groups 1 (alkali metals) and 2 (alkaline earth metals).

seawater: mostly aqueous sodium chloride, with a huge variety of other solutes.

■ It is uneconomic to extract most of the solutes, but bromine is obtained from seawater by oxidising the bromide ions with chlorine. Seawater is too dilute to be used in any electrolytic process requiring brine; *electrolysis* of it produces hydrogen and oxygen rather than chlorine.

secondary alcohol: an *alcohol* where the carbon bearing the –OH group is attached to two other carbon atoms in *alkyl* or aryl groups, which need not be the same.

■ ***e.g.*** The simplest secondary alcohol is propan-2-ol:

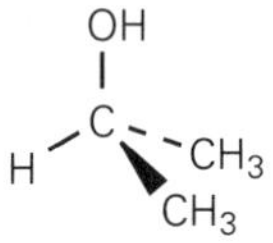

OH
C
H CH_3 CH_3

■ ***TIP*** The term 'secondary' is used in a slightly, but vitally, different sense in the case of alcohols and *amines*. In alcohols the *functional group* –OH does not alter, but in amines the functional group is different for primary, secondary and tertiary amines.

secondary amine: an *amine* where the nitrogen atom bears two *alkyl* or *aryl* groups, which need not be the same.

■ ***e.g.*** Dimethylamine is the simplest secondary amine:

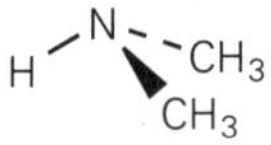

N
H CH_3 CH_3

■ ***TIP*** The term 'secondary' is used in a slightly, but vitally, different sense in the case of alcohols and amines. In alcohols the *functional group* –OH does not alter, but in amines the functional group is different for primary, secondary and tertiary amines.

second electron affinity: the energy change per mole for the process

$$E^-(g) + e^- \longrightarrow E^{2-}(g)$$

■ As two negative species are coming together the process is always endothermic.

second ionisation energy: the energy change per mole for the process

$$E^+(g) \longrightarrow E^{2+}(g) + e^-$$

■ This is always endothermic. This is because the negative electron is being removed from an already positive ion which therefore attracts it.

semiconductor: a material whose conductivity rises with increasing temperature (in contrast to metals where the conductivity falls); it is formed by adding a small amount of impurity to a material that is usually an insulator.

■ ***e.g.*** The most common semiconductor by far is silicon. Extremely pure silicon has a trivalent element such as aluminium added to form a *p*-type semiconductor, or a pentavalent element such as phosphorus added to form an *n*-type semiconductor. If *p–n* junctions are made in the same crystal *lattice* (putting *p*- and *n*-type crystals in contact will not do) then diodes result; *n–p–n* or *p–n–p* junctions produce transistors.

semi-permeable membrane: a membrane which will allow certain materials, but not others, to pass through.

■ ***e.g.*** A common type, Visking, is permeable to water but not to dissolved ions, and an ion-selective membrane is used in the latest modification of the *diaphragm cell* for the production of sodium hydroxide from brine.

shell model of the atom: the model first proposed by Niels Bohr in 1905 where electrons occupy shells of defined energy, identified by the principal *quantum number*, around the nucleus.

■ Electron transition between levels gives rise to *line spectra*.

sigma-bond (also written as 'σ-bond'): a bond formed by head-on overlap between atomic orbitals along an imaginary line joining the nuclei.

■ Single bonds are sigma-bonds; multiple bonds contain a sigma-bond and one or two *pi-bonds*.

silicone: a polymeric organic compound containing chains of silicon alternating with oxygen, with organic groups (which can be *alkyl* or *aryl*) on the silicon atom.

■ Those having short chains are oils, silicone rubbers have some cross-linking of long-chain linear polymers, and silicone resins have a three-dimensional structure. These compounds are extremely heat- and chemical-resistant, and strongly water-repellent.

■ ***e.g.*** The simplest example of a silicone is shown below:

$$HO-Si(CH_3)_2-\left[O-Si(CH_3)_2\right]_n-O-Si(CH_3)_2-OH$$

■ ***TIP*** Because of the silicon–oxygen linkages, the compounds are called siloxanes. The example shown is poly(dimethylsiloxane). These are polymers of the silicon analogues of ketones, e.g. $(CH_3)_2Si{=}O$. Unlike ketones, these polymerise because two Si–O bonds are much stronger than one Si=O. This is not true for two C–O compared with one C=O. The difference lies in the larger size of Si compared to C.

skeletal formula: a formula for organic molecules where the carbon and hydrogen atoms are omitted and only the bonds between them shown; other atoms are shown.

■ The well-known representation of *benzene* is a skeletal formula.

e.g.

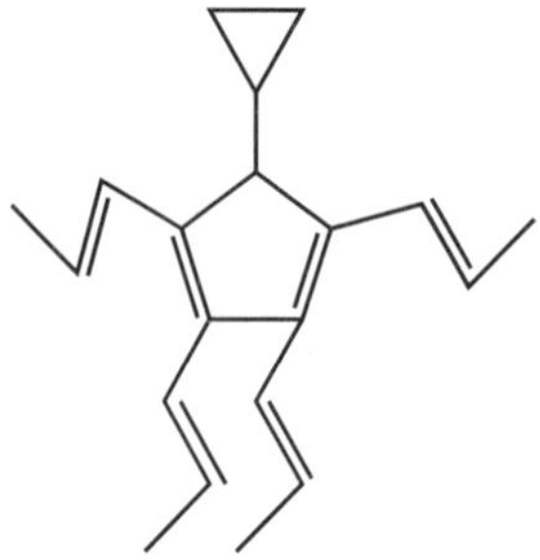

is amusing — and exists

TIP Skeletal formulae are widely used by organic chemists because they are quick to write. Examiners seem to like them less, probably because candidates using them are more prone to make mistakes.

slag: the molten material produced at the same time as molten metal from a blast furnace.

It consists of oxide impurities that have reacted with a flux, which is a material added to produce the impurity as a liquid rather than a solid. It enables the furnace to run continuously because impurities are also removed continuously.

e.g. In iron smelting the flux added is limestone; this decomposes to calcium oxide and carbon dioxide. The basic calcium oxide reacts with acidic impurities in the ore, mainly silica, to give liquid calcium silicate, which is immiscible with the liquid iron:

$$CaO + SiO_2 \longrightarrow CaSiO_3$$

S_N1 (substitution nucleophilic unimolecular): a *nucleophilic substitution* reaction where the rate-determining step depends only on the *concentration* of the species being attacked, and not on the concentration of the *nucleophile*.

It is a *unimolecular reaction* because only one molecule is involved in the *rate-determining step*.

e.g. The reaction between 2-bromo-2-methylpropane and hydroxide ions:

$$(CH_3)_3CBr + OH^- \longrightarrow (CH_3)_3COH + Br^-$$

$$\text{rate} = k[(CH_3)_3CBr]$$

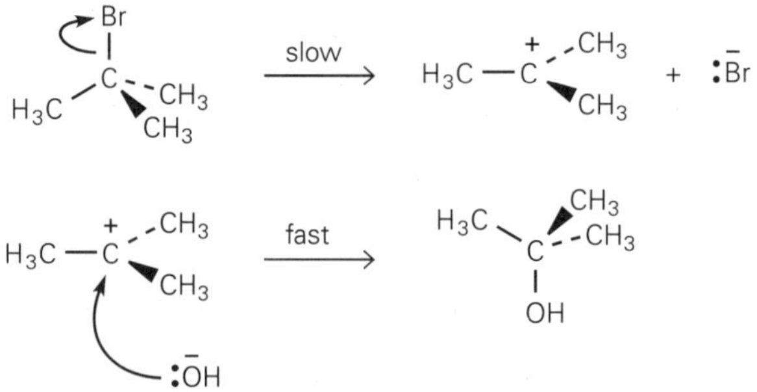

slow

fast

Note that attack on the carbocation will also be from above. If the starting material were chiral, this would lead to a *racemic mixture* as the product.

S_N2 (substitution nucleophilic bimolecular): A *nucleophilic substitution* reaction where the rate-determining step depends on both the *concentration* of the species being attacked and on the concentration of the *nucleophile*.

- It is a *bimolecular reaction* because two species collide in the *rate-determining step*.
- ***e.g.*** The reaction between bromomethane and hydroxide ions:

  $CH_3Br + OH^- \longrightarrow CH_3OH + Br^-$

  rate = $k\,[CH_3Br][OH^-]$

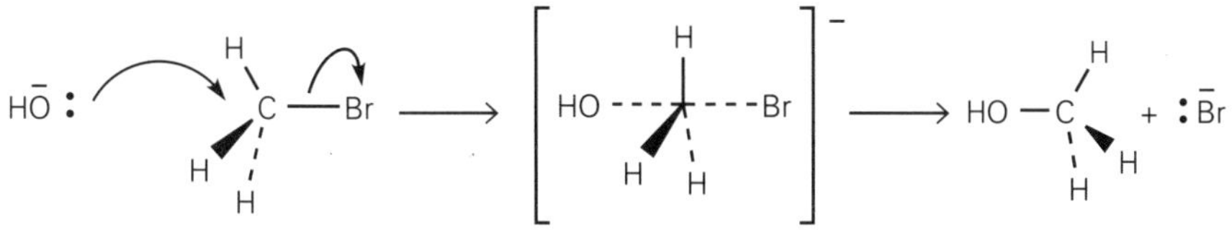

$$HO^- : \; + \; H_3C\text{—}Br \longrightarrow \left[HO\cdots CH_3\cdots Br\right]^- \longrightarrow HO\text{—}CH_3 + :Br^-$$

  If the starting compound were chiral, this reaction would lead to inversion of the molecule — the Walden inversion.

soap: a sodium or potassium salt of a long-chain organic acid.

- Soaps are *emulsifying agents* — they emulsify grease in water, which means they prevent small droplets of the grease from coalescing and forming a separate layer. Sodium salts give solid soaps; potassium salts give liquid soaps.
- ***e.g.*** Soaps are made from a variety of *fats* and oils; sodium stearate, $C_{17}H_{35}COO^-Na^+$, is a common soap and is made via the reaction

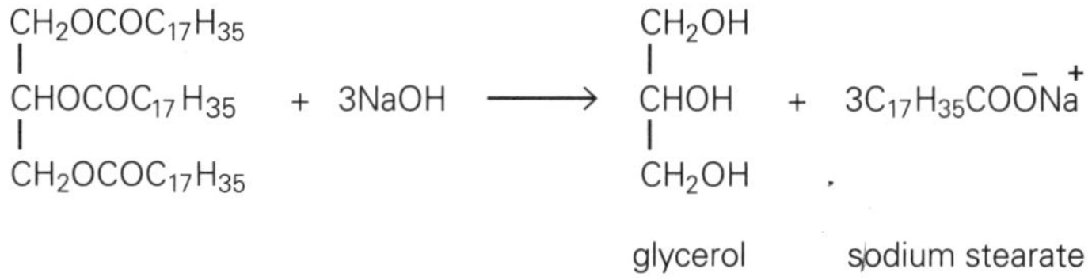

$$\begin{array}{l} CH_2OCOC_{17}H_{35} \\ | \\ CHOCOC_{17}H_{35} \\ | \\ CH_2OCOC_{17}H_{35} \end{array} + 3NaOH \longrightarrow \begin{array}{l} CH_2OH \\ | \\ CHOH \\ | \\ CH_2OH \end{array} + 3C_{17}H_{35}CO\bar{O}\overset{+}{Na}$$

glycerol — sodium stearate

solid: the state of matter characterised by fixed volume and fixed shape.

- Particles in a solid vibrate about mean positions but do not move over large distances. Pure solids are crystalline — they have a regular *lattice* structure. Composite materials such as wood are not crystalline but are certainly solid.
- ***TIP*** Glass, which feels pretty solid, is not crystalline and is regarded as a supercooled liquid.

solubility: the amount of *solute* required to form a *saturated solution* in a given volume of *solvent*.

- Solubility is commonly quoted in mol dm^{-3}, g dm^{-3}, or mol solute per 100 g of solvent.
- ***TIP*** Make sure you know what the units are.

solubility product: for a *sparingly soluble salt* M^+X^- in water, the solubility product is defined as

$$K_s = [M^+][X^-]$$

It is the *equilibrium constant* for the dissolution process:

$$MX(s) \rightleftharpoons M^+(aq) + X^-(aq)$$

In general for a salt M_aX_b

$$K_s = [M^{b+}]^a[X^{a-}]^b$$

with units of $(mol\ dm^{-3})^{a+b}$

e.g. Solubility products at 25°C (in $mol^2\ dm^{-6}$): AgCl, 2.0×10^{-10}; AgI, 8.0×10^{-17}; HgSe, 1.0×10^{-59}.

TIP The value for mercury selenide is interesting because it is hard to see what it means. Apart from being one of the smallest quantities encountered in chemistry, it gives a solubility for HgSe of 3.2×10^{-30} mol dm^{-3}. 10^{-30} mol is 10^{-7} of a molecule, so it suggests that there is only one Hg^{2+} and one Se^{2-} ion in every 10^7 dm^3 (1000 tonnes) of solution. How does one find them? Especially on the laboratory bench.

solute: the substance present in lesser amount in a *solution*.

solution: a mixture of a *solute* dispersed at a molecular or ionic level in a *solvent*.

Most solutions are liquids, but some metals (gold and silver, for example) form solid solutions where the different metal atoms are incorporated in the same crystal *lattice*.

TIP True liquid solutions are always transparent; an opaque liquid is not a solution.

solvation: when ions dissolve in a polar *solvent* such as water, the *polar molecules* of the solvent surround the ions in a layer (which may be several molecules deep) called the solvation shell.

The size of an ion in solution is determined by the size of the solvation shell, and may be much larger than the ionic radius. Small ions of high charge, such as Al^{3+}, are the most heavily solvated because of their high charge density (see also *enthalpy of hydration*).

solvent: the substance present in major amount in a *solution*.

TIP Although this definition is generally true, in some very concentrated solutions, such as sugar syrups, it leads to the idea that the solution is one of water in sugar. However, it isn't always a matter of principle as to which is the solute and which the solvent, it is often a matter of convention. For a solution of a solid in a liquid, the latter is conventionally regarded as the solvent.

solvent extraction: the extraction of a *solute* from *aqueous solution* using an organic solvent in which the solute of interest is more soluble (see also *partition law*).

e.g. A commonly used solvent is ethoxyethane. It is immiscible with water and an excellent solvent for most organic molecules.

***s*-orbital:** the lowest energy orbital in a given *quantum shell*, having spherical symmetry.

sparingly soluble salt: a salt that dissolves to a small extent in water.

■ ***e.g.*** With their solubility in mol dm^{-3}: $BaSO_4$, 9.43×10^{-7}; $CaSO_4$, 4.66×10^{-3}; AgCl, 1.35×10^{-6}.

spectroscopy: a variety of techniques that produce analytical information, usually in the determination of the structure of compounds.

■ Some employ radiation of various sorts (see *infrared, ultraviolet, nuclear magnetic resonance spectrum*), or fragment the molecule and find the masses of the ions, as in the *mass spectrometer.*

spontaneous chemical change: a chemical change which is thermodynamically feasible; that is, one for which the *Gibbs function,* ΔG, is negative.

■ This also means that a *redox* reaction whose overall electrochemical potential is positive will be feasible.

stability: a much-misused word in chemistry — a substance can be stable only with respect to a particular process or reaction.

■ ***e.g.*** Caesium is a perfectly stable element. It does not of itself fall to bits. It is not, however, stable in water.

■ ***TIP*** Avoid the use of 'stable' unless you qualify your meaning.

standard conditions: specified conditions used in *thermodynamics* to ensure that different measurements are comparable.

■ Among the standard conditions are: 1 atm pressure; solids in their most *thermodynamically stable* state; solutions at a concentration of 1 mol dm^{-3}, and a specified temperature. By common usage the temperature has become 298 K unless otherwise stated, but this is not part of the definition of the standard state.

standard electrode: an electrode particularly constructed as a reference for all other electrode potentials.

■ The primary standard electrode is the *standard hydrogen electrode,* which has a defined potential of 0.00 V.

standard electrode potential: the potential of an *electrode* compared with a *standard hydrogen electrode,* where all solutions are at a concentration of 1 mol dm^{-3} and have a pH of zero, gases are at 1 atm pressure, and the temperature is stated.

■ By common usage the temperature has become 298 K unless otherwise stated, but this is not part of the definition of standard conditions. The potentials are quoted as *reduction* potentials in data tables.

■ ***e.g.***

		$E^{\ominus}$/V
$Cu^{2+} + 2e^-$	Cu	+0.34
$Zn^{2+} + 2e^-$	Zn	−0.76

standard hydrogen electrode: the reference electrode for all electrochemical measurements.

■ It consists of a platinum foil coated in platinum black (finely divided platinum) dipping into a solution of hydrochloric acid with $[H^+] = 1$ mol dm^{-3}. Hydrogen gas is bubbled over the surface of the platinum at a pressure of 1 atm. The electrode behaves exactly as an electrode made of (non-conducting) hydrogen would, and allows the equilibrium

$$2H^+(aq) + 2e^- \rightleftharpoons H_2\,(g)$$

to be set up. The electrode has a defined reduction potential at 298 K of 0.00 V.

starch: a *polymer* of glucose.

■ It is principally used as an *indicator* in iodine/thiosulphate *titrations*. As the iodine colour fades to pale yellow, starch is added and the solution turns inky blue. Further titration results in a sharp end point where the mixture suddenly goes colourless. The inky colour is due to a *reversible reaction* between starch and iodine to give 'starch iodide'. This substance has iodine molecules inserted into the polymer's helical structure.

■ ***TIP*** If the starch is added too soon in the titration, an insoluble complex is formed which will not dissociate when thiosulphate ions are added. The titre will therefore be too low.

state: the physical form of a substance.

■ States of interest to the chemist are:

- gas, characterised by both volume and shape being variable. There are large distances between molecules in a gas, and the molecules are free to move over considerable distances compared with their size.
- liquid, characterised by fixed volume but variable shape. Molecules in a liquid can move relative to one another. Many liquids, though, including liquid metals and hydrogen-bonded liquids such as water, have considerable ordering of the molecules.
- solid, characterised by fixed volume and fixed shape. The molecules/ions/atoms in the regularly arranged solid lattice can vibrate about their mean positions, but cannot move over any significant distance.
- aqueous — in solution in water.

■ The solid state is in *equilibrium* with the liquid at the *melting temperature*; the liquid is in equilibrium with the gas at the *boiling temperature*. These three states are in equilibrium at the *triple point*, which is characterised by a unique temperature and pressure for each substance.

state symbols: symbols used in equations to show the *state* of the substances that are taking part in the reaction.

■ (s), (l) and (g) refer to solid, liquid and gas, and (aq) refers to *aqueous solutions*.

■ ***e.g.*** $Na_2CO_3(aq) + 2HCl(aq) \longrightarrow 2NaCl(aq) + H_2O(l) + CO_2(g)$

This should help you to visualise two solutions mixing to form another solution and a gas.

■ ***TIP*** State symbols should be included in examination answers if in doubt, though not in organic reactions where they are not used. They are necessary in *thermochemical equations* and in *redox* equations.

steam distillation: a technique used to purify organic substances that are immiscible with water and which would decompose if distilled conventionally.

- The impure substance is added to water and steam is blown through the mixture. The distillate is a two-*phase* mixture of water and the purified organic material. This can be separated, using a separating funnel or by solvent extraction, and dried.
- ***e.g.*** Macerated orange peel can be steam distilled to produce limonene, an 'essential oil'. Such oils are widely used in the perfume and food industries. Their smell or flavour is generally very sensitive to small amounts of decomposition products, so they are treated as gently as possible, chemically speaking.

steam reforming: the reaction of naphtha (a light petroleum fraction boiling between about 40°C and 150°C) with steam over a platinum/alumina *catalyst* gives a variety of *branched-chain alkanes, cycloalkanes* and *aromatic compounds,* used in the blending of *fuels*. Steam reforming of methane is performed over a nickel oxide/calcium aluminate catalyst at about 750°C and 30 atm pressure. It produces hydrogen and carbon monoxide, the hydrogen being used to manufacture ammonia in the *Haber process*:

$$CH_4(g) + H_2O(g) \longrightarrow CO(g) + 3H_2(g)$$

stereochemistry: the branch of chemistry concerned with molecular shapes.

- ***TIP*** The notion that molecules have shapes was put forward by the Dutch chemist J. H. van't Hoff. He was publicly derided for this idea by the great German chemist Hermann Kolbe in 1882; sadly Kolbe did not live to see van't Hoff receive the first Nobel prize for chemistry in 1901.

stereoisomerism: isomerism resulting from differences in the shapes of molecules brought about by restricted rotation (*cis–trans* isomerism) or by molecules having non-superimposable mirror images (optical isomerism).

- ***e.g.*** The top example in the diagram below shows *cis–trans* isomerism in 1,2-dichloroethene; the bottom one shows the non-superimposable mirror-image pair of butan-2-ol.

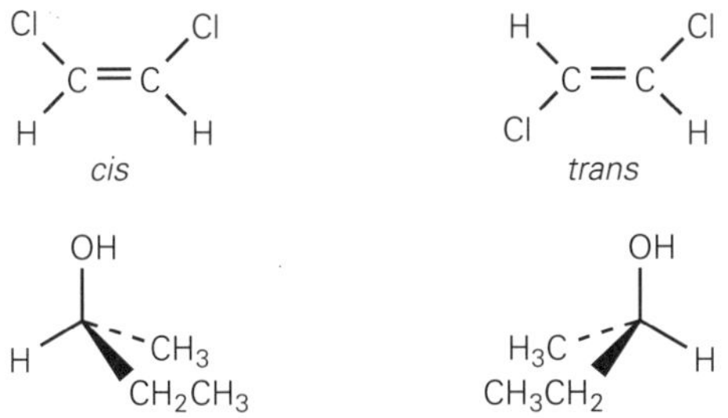

cis *trans*

steric hindrance: the prevention or slowing down of some reactions by atoms or groups blocking the access of an attacking molecule or ion and so stopping it from getting close enough to the atom it would have attacked.

e.g. The resistance to *hydrolysis* of CCl_4 is partly due to steric hindrance; the large chlorine atoms block access of the attacking water molecule to the carbon atom. $SiCl_4$ is rapidly hydrolysed because the larger silicon atom spaces out the chorine atoms and allows the water to get in.

stoichiometry: either the ratio in which elements combine in a compound, or the ratio in which compounds react in a reaction.

e.g. Sodium oxide, Na_2O, has a stoichiometry of 2:1. The reaction between iron and chlorine to give iron(III) chloride

$$2Fe(s) + 3Cl_2(g) \longrightarrow 2FeCl_3(s)$$

has a stoichiometry of 2:3.

storage cell: an *electrochemical cell* that stores (as chemical energy) useful amounts of electrical energy.

All commercial batteries are storage cells (see *lead–acid battery*).

strong acid: an acid that is completely ionised in solution.

For an acid that has several ionisation steps, such as sulphuric acid, it is only the first ionisation that is strong.

e.g. Nitric acid; hydrochloric acid; chloric(VII) acid, $HClO_4$.

structural isomerism: the very common form of isomerism where molecules have the same molecular formula but different molecular structure, and do not show other forms of isomerism, such as geometric or optical.

e.g. The simplest example is that of butane $CH_3CH_2CH_2CH_3$ and 2-methylpropane $CH_3CH(CH_3)CH_3$.

sublimation: the *phase* transition from a *solid* to a *gas* without an intervening *liquid* stage.

Most covalent substances will sublime if the pressure is below that of the *triple point*, so only those substances which have a triple point pressure higher than 1 atm sublime under ordinary conditions.

e.g. Solid carbon dioxide; ice sublimes under reduced pressure in the technique of *freeze-drying*.

substitution reaction: reaction in which an atom or group of atoms in a molecule is replaced by another atom or group.

Apart from burning, it is the only type of reaction that *saturated compounds* can undergo.

e.g.

- radical substitution: $CH_4 + Cl_2 \longrightarrow CH_3Cl + HCl$
- nucleophilic substitution: $CH_3Br + NaOH \longrightarrow CH_3OH + NaBr$
- electrophilic substitution:

$$C_6H_6 + Cl_2 \xrightarrow{AlCl_3} C_6H_5Cl + HCl$$

supercooling: cooling a *liquid* below its normal *freezing temperature* without it changing state.

- It requires the absence of nuclei on which crystals tend to form, such as dust particles. Shaking a supercooled liquid will often cause it to crystallise.
- ***e.g.*** A particularly unusual and striking form of a supercooled liquid is *glass* — a mixture of calcium and sodium silicates, it does not have a crystalline structure.

superoxide: a compound containing the O_2^- ion.

- This ion has an unpaired electron and is therefore a *radical* anion.
- ***e.g.*** Superoxides are formed by the larger atoms in group 1 when burnt in oxygen: KO_2 (yellow), RbO_2 (orange), CsO_2 (red).

surface active agent (also called 'surfactant')**:** a substance fulfilling the same role as *soaps* by emulsifying the grease with which dirt is usually associated, holding the oil droplets in suspension so that they can be washed away (see *emulsifying agent*).

- Unlike soaps, they do not form a scum with *hard water*. There are three types:
  - Anionic surfactants are based on alkylbenzenesulphonates (below left), used in products such as washing powders, or alkyl sulphates (below right), which are used in toothpaste, shampoos and shower gels.

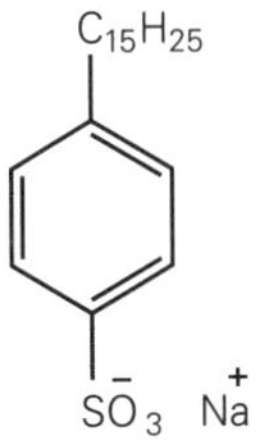

$C_{15}H_{25}$ (benzene ring) $SO_3^-\ Na^+$

$C_{12}H_{25}O—SO_2—OH$

  - Cationic surfactants have lower activity than anionic surfactants and are used in fabric softeners and in hair conditioners. An example is $C_{15}H_{31}CH_2N^+(CH_3)_3Br^-$.
  - Non-ionic surfactants are ethoxylates such as $CH_3(CH_2)_{10}CH_2(OCH_2CH_2)_8OH$. They are more active than anionic surfactants at similar concentrations and work well in cold or cool water. They are found in liquid and powder fabric detergents and in surface cleaners, and represent over half of all surfactant production.
- ***TIP*** Surfactants are also known as *detergents* although, in fact, they are only part of a detergent's composition.

synthesis: a series of reactions giving a desired chemical product.

- Originally it specifically meant the preparation of a compound from its elements.

tertiary alcohol: an *alcohol* in which the carbon bearing the –OH group is attached to three other carbon atoms, i.e. to three *alkyl* or *aryl* groups, which need not be the same.

■ ***e.g.*** The simplest tertiary alcohol is 2-methylpropan-2-ol:

OH
C
H_3C CH_3
CH_3

tetrahedral: the disposition of bonds about an atom having four bonding pairs of electrons and no *lone pairs*.

■ ***e.g.*** 2-methylpropan-2-ol has a tetrahedral carbon atom at its centre (see *tertiary alcohol*).

theoretical yield: the yield that would be expected from a reaction if there were no losses at all.

■ As there are usually competing reactions (in organic chemistry, anyway) and handling losses are inevitable in most preparative chemistry, the actual yield is seldom better than 90% of the theoretical yield. The exception is in quantitative *gravimetric analysis*, where careful choice of the analytical reagents and meticulous attention to the detail of technique should lead to the theoretical yield of the precipitate being obtained within experimental error.

thermal decomposition: the decomposition of a substance by heating.

■ ***e.g.*** Heating lead nitrate causes it to decompose in a non-reversible reaction:

$$2Pb(NO_3)_2 \longrightarrow 2PbO(s) + 4NO_2(g) + O_2(g)$$

thermal dissociation: the process whereby a substance decomposes on heating but is regenerated on cooling — provided it has been heated in a closed system and the products have not disappeared.

■ ***e.g.*** Dinitrogen tetroxide dissociates to nitrogen dioxide on heating, but is reformed on cooling:

$$N_2O_4(g) \rightleftharpoons 2NO_2(g)$$

thermal stability: a rather loose term relating to the resistance of a substance to decomposition on heating.

thermochemical equation: a chemical equation that shows not only the reaction occurring but also the associated *enthalpy* change.

e.g. $H^+(aq) + OH^-(aq) \longrightarrow H_2O(l) \quad \Delta H = -57\ kJ\ mol^{-1}$

thermochemistry: the study of heat changes occurring during chemical reactions.

These can be shown in a *thermochemical equation.*

e.g. $H^+(aq) + OH^-(aq) \longrightarrow H_2O(l) \quad \Delta H = -57\ kJ\ mol^{-1}$

thermodynamics: that branch of natural philosophy which deals with heat changes, *entropy* changes and *free energy* changes.

It is enshrined in the three laws of thermodynamics.

(1) First law of thermodynamics: essentially, this is the law of conservation of energy; that is, energy can neither be created nor destroyed, but can only be changed from one form into another. *Thermochemistry* comes from the first law.

(2) Second law of thermodynamics: this states that heat cannot pass from a cold body to a warmer body without work being provided from some external source. An alternative view is that any system will change in such a way as to increase the *entropy* of the universe. Entropy can be identified with disorder, so all *spontaneous chemical changes* increase the disorder of the universe.

(3) Third law of thermodynamics: this states that the entropy for a perfect crystal at 0 K is zero.

TIP The three laws of thermodynamics have been amusingly summarised:

- the first law says you can't win, you can only break even
- the second law says you can only break even at absolute zero
- the third law says you can't reach absolute zero

thermodynamic stability: a term of comparison between *reagents* and products in a chemical reaction.

An approximate view is that a mixture is thermodynamically stable if reaction would lead to an *endothermic* change. Whether it actually reacts depends on other factors, particularly the *activation energy* for the reaction and the conditions.

e.g. A mixture of nitrogen and oxygen is thermodynamically stable with respect to nitrogen monoxide:

$$N_2(g) + O_2(g) \longrightarrow 2NO(g) \quad \Delta H^{\ominus} = +90.4\ kJ\ mol^{-1}$$

TIP This definition ignores the *entropy* contribution, but if you don't study entropy it is difficult to include it! True thermodynamic stability is when the Gibbs function or Gibbs free energy change, $\Delta G^{\ominus}$, for the reaction is positive.

titration (also called 'volumetric analysis')**:** an analytical technique used to determine the concentration of a solution.

A *solution* of known *concentration* is run from a burette into a solution of known volume. When a particular colour change occurs in the solution, due to the presence of an added *indicator*, the burette tap is closed. The initial and final readings on the burette give the volume of the added liquid (the titrant). Knowing the volume of both solutions and the concentration of one of them enables the concentration of the other to be calculated from a knowledge of the reaction occurring. Titration can be adapted to run automatically.

e.g. There are many possible analyses that can be done by titration, including acids with bases (hydrochloric acid and sodium hydroxide, say), reducing agents with oxidising agents (potassium manganate(VII) with iron(II) ions, say, or iodine with sodium thiosulphate), and *precipitation reactions* (chloride ions with silver nitrate, for example).

TIP Titrations can also be performed by measuring temperature changes in the reaction mixture as the titrant is added (thermometric titration), or by measuring the conductivity of the reaction mixture (conductimetric titration).

titration curve: a plot of the pH of the reaction mixture against the amount of titrant added.

In the case of acid–base titrations, the *indicator* is chosen so that the pH range over which it changes colour falls on the steep part of the titration curve.

e.g. The titration curve shown below is for the addition of base to acid.

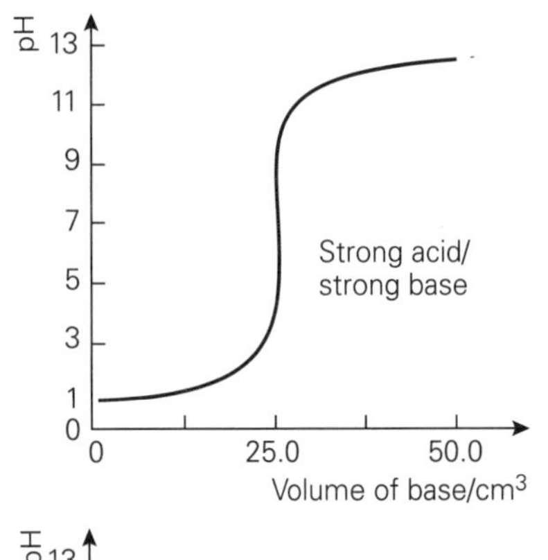

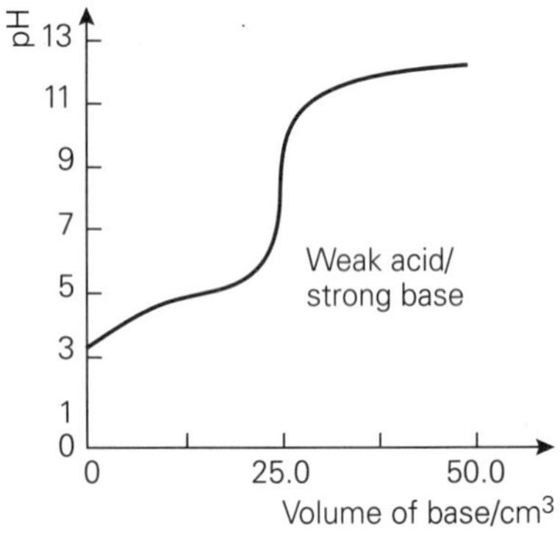

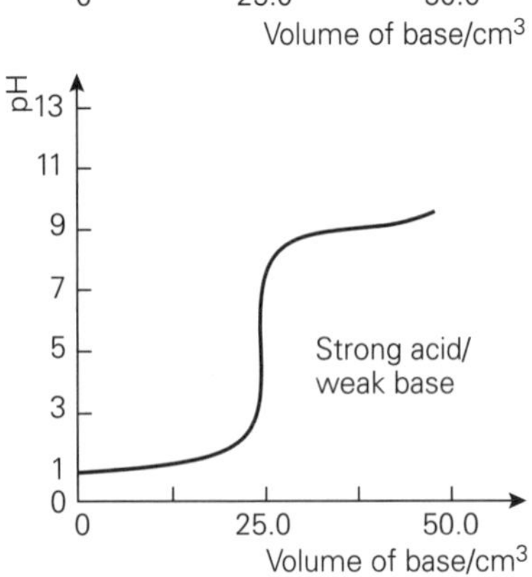

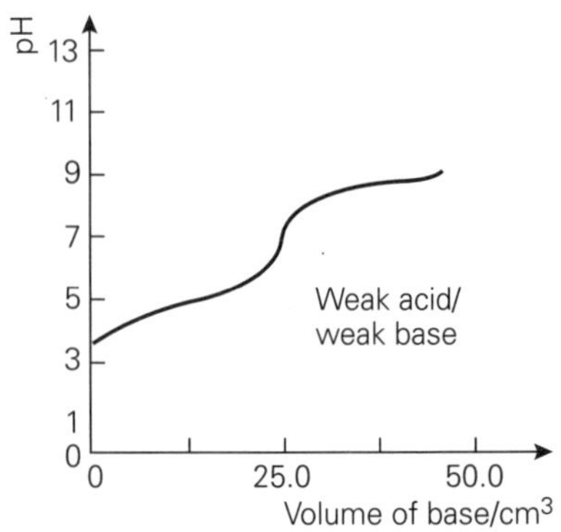

Tollen's reagent: an alkaline solution of silver nitrate which is reduced to a silver mirror by aldehydes.

- Tollen's reagent is made by first precipitating silver oxide from silver nitrate solution using sodium hydroxide solution, and then dissolving the precipitate in ammonia. It will work at room temperature, unlike *ammoniacal silver nitrate solution*, which requires warming.

transition metal: a metallic element which has at least one of its ions with a partly filled *d*-shell.

- ***e.g.*** The transition metals are $_{22}Ti$ to $_{29}Cu$, $_{40}Zr$ to $_{47}Ag$, $_{58}Ce$ to $_{79}Au$, and the elements beyond $_{90}Th$.
- ***TIP*** The definition of the term has changed over the years; in Mendeleev's view, the transition elements were the elements of group 8: Fe, Co, Ni, Tc, Ru, Rh, Os, Ir and Pt.

transition state: the high-energy structure through which the reactants must pass in order to become products.

- It is the structure of the species present at the peak of the *reaction profile*.

trigonal bipyramid: the structure formed by a molecule whose central atom has five bond pairs and no *lone pairs*, such as in gaseous PF_5 (below left).

- It is the basis for all molecules where the central atom has five pairs of electrons. Lone pairs are always found in the equatorial plane, so chlorine trifluoride has a T-shape (below right).
- ***e.g.***

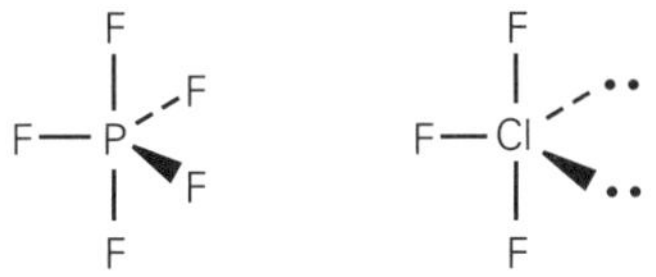

trigonal planar: the structure formed by a molecule whose central atom has three bond pairs and no *lone pairs*.

- ***e.g.*** BF_3 is one such molecule:

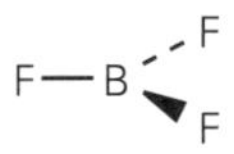

triple point: the unique temperature and pressure at which all three phases of a substance, *solid, liquid* and *gas*, are in *equilibrium*.

- ***e.g.*** The triple point of water is at a temperature of 0.01°C and a pressure of 6.03×10^{-3} atm; that of carbon dioxide is –56.55°C and 5.11 atm.

ultraviolet (UV): that part of the electromagnetic spectrum that lies at wavelengths immediately shorter than the visible violet.

■ It corresponds to wavelengths around 10^{-8} m or frequencies around 3×10^{16} Hz. Ultraviolet light is used in the photochemical halogenation of *alkanes*, splitting chlorine molecules into *radicals* by *homolytic fission.*

unimolecular reaction: a reaction where the rate-determining step involves only one species.

■ ***e.g.*** The S_N1 reaction of 2-bromo-2-methylpropane with hydroxide ions is unimolecular:

$$(CH_3)_3C\text{–}Br \xrightarrow{\text{slow}} (CH_3)_3C^+ + :Br^-$$

$$(CH_3)_3C^+ + :OH^- \xrightarrow{\text{fast}} (CH_3)_3C\text{–}OH$$

■ ***TIP*** A unimolecular reaction is not necessarily a first order reaction; it will not be unless the *rate-determining step* is also the first step in the mechanism.

unsaturated compound: a compound that contains carbon–carbon double or triple bonds, and which can therefore undergo addition reactions.

■ ***e.g.*** The alkenes $RCH=CH_2$ and the alkynes $RC\equiv CR$ are unsaturated compounds. They can add hydrogen, for example. The origin of the term is that the molecules are unsaturated with hydrogen, unlike the alkanes.

■ ***TIP*** Do not confuse the term 'unsaturated' as applied to compounds with the same word (and its inverse) as applied to solutions.

urea (also called 'carbamide')**:** the compound $(H_2N)_2C=O$.

■ It is the main nitrogenous excretory product from most mammals. It is used as a fertiliser.

valence shell: the outer shell of an atom containing the electrons that are used in bonding, outside the *noble gas* core electron structure.

- ***e.g.*** The valence shell is shown in bold:

  Na $1s^2 2s^2 2p^6 \mathbf{3s^1}$

  Si $1s^2 2s^2 2p^6 \mathbf{3s^2 3p^2}$

  Fe $1s^2 2s^2 2p^6 3s^2 3p^2 3p^6 \mathbf{3d^6 4s^2}$

valence shell electron-pair repulsion theory: a theory used to predict the shapes of molecules.

- The shape of a covalent molecule about a particular atom centre depends on the number of electron pairs around that atom; the electron pairs arrange themselves to be as far apart as is possible, thus minimising repulsions. *Lone pair orbitals* are rather fatter than bond pair orbitals, so have a greater repulsive force.
- ***e.g.*** Methane, ammonia and water are all based on a tetrahedral arrangement of four pairs of electrons. Methane is a regularly tetrahedral molecule, having four equivalent bond pairs and a H–C–H bond angle of almost 109.5°. Ammonia has one lone pair and three bond pairs, the lone pair forcing the latter closer together so that the H–N–H bond angle is about 107°. Water has two lone pairs and two bond pairs, and the H–O–H bond angle is around 104°.

van der Waals forces: weak and rather short-range *intermolecular forces* that arise from the interaction of temporary dipole–temporary dipole attractions.

- ***TIP*** van der Waals forces increase with increasing size of the molecules. This is why the melting and boiling temperatures for compounds in a *homologous series* rise as the series is ascended.

van't Hoff isochore: if the *equilibrium constant* for a reaction is known at two different temperatures, then the *enthalpy change* for the reaction can be found from the van't Hoff isochore:

$$\ln(K_1/K_2) = (\Delta H/R)(1/T_2 - 1/T_1)$$

- This can also be used to explain the effect of a change in temperature on the *equilibrium* composition of a reaction if ΔH is known. (See also *Le Chatelier's principle*.)

■ ***TIP*** The temperatures must be in K. The calculation assumes that ΔH is constant over the temperature range concerned; this will generally be true.

vapour: the gaseous form of a substance at temperatures below the *boiling temperature*, usually used where the substance is not boiling but is evaporating.

■ ***TIP*** Strictly, the vapour is that gaseous state of a substance below its critical temperature. The critical temperature is that temperature above which a gas cannot be liquefied by application of pressure alone.

vapour pressure: the pressure of a vapour above a liquid.

■ If the system is sealed and is at equilibrium at a particular temperature, the vapour pressure is then the *saturated vapour pressure*.

visible spectrophotometer: a spectrophotometer that operates in the visible region of the electromagnetic spectrum.

■ The wavelength of the light is more precisely determined than in a *colorimeter*, and the visible spectrophotometer scans the whole range of the visible spectrum. A graph of absorbance vs wavelength is then produced.

volumetric analysis: see *titration*.

Walden inversion: *nucleophilic substitution* of a *chiral molecule* via an S_N2 reaction leads to an inversion of the three groups not affected by the substitution.

- If chiral molecules of a single orientation are being used in synthetic processes, it is important to know if such inversions occur. Otherwise, the stereochemistry of the products may be incorrect.
- ***e.g.*** The reaction of hydroxide ions with 2-bromobutane to give butan-2-ol:

H
$H\bar{O}:$ — Br
H_3C
C_2H_5
⟶
H
HO —
CH_3
C_2H_5
$:\bar{Br}$

washing soda: sodium carbonate decahydrate, $Na_2CO_3.10H_2O$.

- This is used to soften *hard water* because the calcium ions in solution are precipitated as calcium carbonate.

water, H_2O: a strongly hydrogen-bonded liquid at room temperature, it is easily the most significant *solvent* in chemistry, though it reacts with many inorganic and organic compounds by *hydrolysis*.

- Its *melting* and *boiling temperatures* at standard pressure are the fixed points for the *Celsius scale* of temperature.

water of crystallisation: water molecules that are incorporated into the crystal *lattice* of many inorganic salts when they crystallise from *aqueous solution*.

- ***e.g.*** $CuSO_4.5H_2O$; $FeSO_4.6H_2O$; $Na_2CO_3.10H_2O$; and many others.
- ***TIP*** The crystals usually look glassy — copper(II) sulphate crystals used to be called blue vitriol for this reason. The crystals do not feel wet!

wave number: the reciprocal of wavelength, $1/\lambda$.

- It is the number of waves in a unit length, and is mostly used in infrared spectroscopy where the units are cm^{-1} (see *infrared spectrum*).

weak acid: an acid that is partly dissociated in *aqueous solution*.

- The extent of the dissociation depends on the acid concentration, but ethanoic acid is typically about 2% dissociated. Weak acids have a K_a value that is of the order of 10^{-3} mol dm^{-3} or less.

e.g. Ethanoic acid, citric acid and most other organic acids. Carbonic acid, H_2CO_3, and sulphurous acid, H_2SO_3, are weak inorganic acids.

TIP Don't forget that 'weak' and 'dilute' do not have the same meaning. Concentrated solutions of ethanoic acid are still weak, in that they are partially dissociated.

Wheland intermediate: the intermediate ion in the *electrophilic substitution* of benzene and its derivatives.

e.g. The Wheland intermediate in the *nitration* of benzene has the structure:

+ NO_2 H

work hardening: working a *metal* at room temperature often causes its physical properties to change; principally it hardens and increases in strength.

Work hardening can be a problem if a metal needs to remain soft but becomes harder due to vibration, say, as it may then fracture.

e.g. Bending a sheet of brass is easy; try to bend it back and it will probably break, having hardened considerably.

Xenon: one of the *noble gases* (the elements from group 0 of the periodic table) that is notable for having a fairly extensive chemistry.

- For decades everybody had assumed that the noble gases were truly inert. In 1960, however, Bartlett simply mixed fluorine with xenon and within a few hours had crystals of XeF_4.
- ***TIP*** All xenon compounds contain fluorine, oxygen, or both.

X-ray: electromagnetic radiation of wavelength around 10^{-10} m, with an energy around 10^6 kJ mol^{-1}.

X-ray crystallography: a technique used to determine the structures of crystals.

- If *X-rays* are passed through a single crystal of a substance, the radiation is reflected from planes in the crystals. This leads to interference patterns where the waves either reinforce or cancel. Rotating the crystal in an X-ray beam and monitoring the reflected radiation by, say, a photographic film, enables the structure of the crystal to be determined. This has now been done for even very complex structures, such as haemoglobin.

zeolite: a naturally occurring aluminosilicate rock that contains cations in the cavities of the aluminosilicate framework.

- These ions can easily be exchanged with other ions in solution, and zeolites containing sodium ions found wide use as ion-exchange materials for water softening before the development of synthetic alternatives. They are still used as drying agents.

Ziegler–Natta catalyst: a complex *catalyst* containing titanium and organo-aluminium compounds such as $Al(CH_2CH_2CH_2CH_3)_3$.

- Such catalysts catalyse the polymerisation of *alkenes* in a way that makes the resulting chains very regular stereochemically.
- ***e.g.*** Poly(propene) can be made with all of the methyl groups on the same side of the *polymer* chain. This gives a more crystalline polymer, which is harder and more transparent than non-crystalline varieties.

zone refining: a technique for producing extremely pure metals or silicon.

- ***e.g.*** A bar of silicon is heated over a narrow zone so that it melts; the molten zone is slowly moved along the bar. Impurities tend to remain in the molten part and so are moved to the end of the bar, which can be discarded. Used especially to produce very high purity silicon for the semiconductor industry.

zwitterion: an ion, typically found with *amino acids*, which has both a positive and a negative charge.

R
R'
COO^-
NH_3^+

- ***TIP*** The strong *intermolecular forces* between these ions give amino acids an unusually high *melting temperature* for their size. The amino acid glycine, H_2NCH_2COOH, has a melting temperature of 232°C; propanoic acid, CH_3CH_2COOH, is a similar size and melts at –20.8°C.

zymase: a colloquial term for the mixture of *enzymes* found in yeast that converts sugars to ethanol; it is not by any means a single enzyme.